GW00390935

ATTACK AT NIGHT

ATTACK
AT NIGHT

Robert Jackson

Weidenfeld and Nicolson
London

2.9.7 P

Published in Great Britain in 1988 by
George Weidenfeld & Nicolson Limited
91 Clapham High Street, London sw4 7ta

isbn 0 297 79308 x

Printed in Great Britain by
Butler & Tanner Ltd,
Frome and London

CHAPTER ONE

The pilot of the big four-engined Short Sunderland flying boat gave a slight start as a hand tapped him on the shoulder, then looked up, smiled, and reached out to take the enamel mug of coffee that was being offered to him by one of the crew.

It was three hours since the Sunderland had lifted away from the waters of Plymouth Sound and set course south-westwards into the Atlantic, flying under a grey December sky. The island of Ushant off the Brest Peninsula, marking the most westerly point of German-occupied Europe, was well astern now, invisible in the murk that veiled the horizon, and now the flying boat was cruising over the outer limits of the Bay of Biscay.

The pilot was a squadron leader and, like the twelve members of his crew, came from the sunnier climes of Australia. He was an old flying boat hand, having captained the magnificent 'Empire' Class boats – from which the Sunderland had been developed – with Qantas on the Singapore to Darwin run before the war.

Now, in December 1943, the war was in its fifth year, and showed no sign of ending. As far as the flying boat skipper and his crew were concerned, war meant the monotony of endless hours droning over the ocean, protecting the vital Atlantic convoys from the ever-present menace of Hitler's U-boats. In all those hours the Australian crew had sighted two enemy submarines and succeeded in attacking one of them, with unknown results. On the second attack, the depth-charges had hung up through an electrical fault and the U-boat had got away unscathed. Other crews had been luckier, particularly in the early part of 1943, when shore-based RAF aircraft, equipped with new detection gear and operating in conjunction with the Royal Navy's 'hunter-killer' groups, had at last begun to get the measure of the underwater threat.

Successes had continued to mount steadily throughout the year, especially in the North Atlantic, where the German 'wolfpacks' had taken a severe hammering. In September and October alone, British, Canadian and American aircraft and warships had destroyed no fewer than twenty-five U-boats, while they themselves had sunk only nine merchant ships.

Beaten in the North Atlantic, the U-boats were now concentrating in more southerly waters, preying on the north-south convoys from Freetown and Gibraltar. In October and November two convoys had been attacked as they passed the notorious Bay of Biscay, but two U-boats had been sunk by the escorting warships and all the Germans had to show for their efforts was one merchant ship damaged.

'Navigator to pilot.'

The squadron leader put a hand to his face mask, which had been dangling loosely, and placed it over his mouth, flicking the intercom switch as he did so.

'Go ahead, nav.'

'We will be at position forty-six north, zero nine west in fifteen minutes, skippper. Should be sighting the convoy shortly, if it's where it should be.'

The pilot grunted over the intercom. 'Roger. Can't see anything yet. It's very hazy up ahead, and the cloud seems to be getting lower. Keep your eyes peeled, lookouts.' He glanced at his co-pilot, a very young flying officer who was sitting in the right-hand seat. This was his first operational trip, and the squadron leader had decided to take him under his wing for a while.

'Take over for a minute, Dickie. I'm going back for a pee.'

The boy's face brightened at being given the responsibility. 'Right, skipper. I've got her.'

The Sunderland's captain grinned and winked at him as he undid his harness and clambered out of his seat. Can't do much harm anyway, he thought as he moved back along the fuselage towards the Elsan toilet. The Sunderland was flying on autopilot.

Behind the two pilots' seats, the Sunderland's flight-deck crew of navigator, radio operator and flight engineer were all busy at their stations. The captain went past them and along the companionway, passing the beam gunners and the mid-upper. The Sunderland had a powerful defensive armament of fourteen ·303 Browning machine-guns, and needed it; the big boats sometimes had to fight off attacks by enemy Junkers 88s over the Bay of Biscay.

A few minutes later, feeling much relieved, the captain made his way back to the flight deck and resumed control. The ASV radar operator, whose task it was to detect ships or U-boats on the surface, had nothing to report, which was puzzling; the convoy ought to have been within radar range by now.

The Sunderland crews of RAF Coastal Command generally preferred convoy protection duty to anti-submarine patrols. At least, circling protectively around a convoy, there was something to look at, something to relieve the boredom of long hours spent quartering the sea, all too often with no result.

The convoy which the Sunderland was on its way to meet was a big one, even by the standards of 1943. In fact it was two in one: SL142 from Sierra Leone, combined with MKS36 from Gibraltar – sixty-six ships in all, homeward bound for the United Kingdom under a heavy escort of destroyers, sloops and a single small aircraft carrier.

On the first day of December, as the convoy battled its way through heaving Atlantic seas, passing latitude forty-four degrees north on its homeward run, lookouts sighted a distant black speck in the eastern sky and knew it for what it was: a Focke-Wulf Kondor long-range reconnaissance aircraft. The little carrier – a converted merchant vessel – launched two of her six Grumman Martlet fighters in desperation to intercept the enemy, but the Kondor escaped into cloud long before they got within striking distance.

The grizzled skipper of one of the freighters, a veteran of forty years at sea and an old hand on the Atlantic convoys in two world wars, settled his greasy cap more firmly on his head and sucked hard on his unlit pipe before removing it from his mouth and turning to the mate, who was studying a chart and trying to stay upright on the heaving bridge. The mate was a much younger man, and this was his first convoy run in the Atlantic; he had previously been on the East African run, from Mogadishu to Durban, before crossing the continent to join this ship at Sierra Leone as a replacement. He was UK-bound in any case, and his predecessor was still in hospital in Freetown, recovering from the effects of a bar-room brawl.

The skipper, seeing the mate hunched and shivering in his duffle coat, grinned before speaking. His accent betrayed his origins in the Yorkshire port of Hull, from where he had first taken ship in a trawler at the age of fifteen.

'Feeling t' cold, lad? Never mind, things'll warm up soon enough. They allus do, after yon buggers put in an appearance.' He waved his pipe in the direction of the cloud into which the Focke-Wulf had recently disappeared. 'Bay o' bloody Biscay,' he went on, jabbing a finger at the mate's chart. 'Forty-four north to forty-eight. The buggers'll give us hell for the next couple of days, until we're abeam Ushant. Then the Air Force will come out to look after us – when it's too bloody late, as usual.'

The skipper was being less than fair on the RAF, but he found it hard to shake off the terrible experiences of the early war years, when no air cover had been available and convoys had been decimated. Besides, he had a nasty feeling in his gut that the Germans would go all out to hit this convoy hard. He was right. But this time, the threat would not come from beneath the waves.

Twenty-four hours later, as the Sunderland flew southwards to make its rendezvous, it was the keen-eyed co-pilot who saw the first sign of the disaster that had overwhelmed the ships.

It looked at first like a dark and threatening cloud, drifting low over the horizon. But as the Sunderland drew closer, the men in the cockpit could see that the base of the cloud was shot with red in places. Minutes later, the cloud had resolved itself into several distinct columns, merging higher up into a single spreading pall that fanned out slowly before the easterly wind.

Stunned, the Sunderland's crew gazed down on the carnage. The sea was littered with dying ships, many of them fiercely ablaze. Dense black smoke boiled up from stricken oil tankers, their shattered hulls surrounded by circles of burning fuel in which men screamed and died. Some freighters, which must have been carrying chemical cargoes, burned with a fierce multicoloured light. The escort carrier was listing heavily, but not heavily enough to have lost her aircraft overboard. Yet there was no sign of them.

The Sunderland circled the remnants of the convoy slowly. The pilots counted twenty-two vessels, either sinking or so severely damaged that it was doubtful if they could be saved. Vessels which had escaped unharmed, or apparently so, were scattered all over the ocean. The destroyer escorts were scurrying to and fro like sheepdogs, trying to restore some order from the confusion. Others were stopped in the water, braving any danger from prowling U-boats in order to pick up survivors. The flying boat's signaller tried to contact one of the warships by Aldis lamp, but got no response.

'Never seen anything like this before,' the Australian squadron leader muttered. 'Can't have been an attack by a pack of U-boats, or there'd be ships trailing back for fifty miles. This lot is concentrated in just a few square miles of sea. The carrier has obviously launched her aircraft, so it must have been an air strike – but I've never seen damage like this caused by one air attack.'

'Couldn't have been a battleship or something, could it?' ventured the co-pilot. The flying boat skipper shook his head. 'No – if you remember the *Tirpitz* was damaged by our midget subs a few weeks ago in Norway, and the *Scharnhorst* is still in Altenfjord. Or at least she was yesterday, according to the latest Intelligence reports. Couldn't have got down here, unless she flew. Their only other seaworthy battle-wagon, the *Lützow*, is holed up in the Baltic. So it must have been an air attack, hence the absence of the carrier's fighters. The poor beggars have probably run out of fuel.'

The Sunderland flew over a spreading patch of oil which marked the grave of a ship. A dozen or so men were swimming away from it, some helping others to stay afloat.

The Sunderland's captain quickly made up his mind. Turning the big aircraft, he began a low-level run back towards the struggling survivors and instructed his crew to drop the aircraft's rear dinghy, which would hold seven men. There was no hesitation in obeying his order, even though it meant that the airmen's own chances of survival could be greatly diminished.

Below, the elderly merchant captain from Hull, who had just had his ship blown from under him for the third time in this war, saw the dinghy pack hit the water and began to strike out towards it, dragging the mate with him. The younger man had a bad gash in his scalp and was barely conscious.

'Come on, lad,' the skipper gasped, spitting out a mouthful of salt water. 'Bear up, now. We'll be all right. Told you the buggers were always late.'

Not that they could have done much about it this time, he thought bitterly.

Four hundred miles south-east of the Bay of Biscay, the winter sun that had shone wanly through the smoke of the burning convoy now reflected from the salt marshes of the Camargue, highlighting their pastel shades of green and dun; but the sun was weaker now, for time had passed and December was well advanced.

The *gardien*'s sturdy white horse shifted restlessly and he clucked his tongue at it. It understood and resumed its statue-like stance, head down slightly, a tremor of pleasure passing through it as the rider stroked its neck briefly.

The *gardien* sat easily and solidly in the saddle, which consisted of a cantle in the form of a back rest and a very high pommel. It was flanked by two saddle bags. He held his chest slightly in, his legs stretched almost at full length, feet resting firmly in the stirrups – solid metal cages that were peculiar to the Camargue horsemen – with his heels turned outwards. His left hand grasped the *mourraioun*, the traditional lasso which, knotted around the horse's muzzle, also served as a bridle.

Nowhere else in France, perhaps not even in the whole of Europe, was there a region as haunting as the Camargue, that three-hundred-square-mile area of lagoons and marshy plains nestling in the heart of the Rhône delta. Here, amid this wild and lonely scenery, flourished thirty ranches, each with its own *manade*, or herd, of white horses and small black bulls.

The bulls came originally from Asia, but no one could say for sure where the horses had their origins. Some said that they were first imported to the Camargue by the Carthaginians and that later the Romans, impressed by the animals' stamina, bred them to provide mounts for their auxiliary cavalry. Another theory was that they came from Chinese Turkestan with the Huns, the terrible cavalry from the Steppes, whose drive westwards had pushed other barbarian tribes before them like a floodtide, to batter against and finally break the defences of the Roman Empire.

The *gardien* had often turned his mind to these things during his lonely vigil in all weathers, watching over the bulls that were his responsibility. It was in the nature of his people not to take things for granted, but to learn and to inquire. Secretly, though, he preferred the tale his grandmother had told him, long ago; that the first white horses of the Camargue were born out of the Mediterranean foam. It was easy to believe, when one watched the horses galloping wild and free along the shore, manes and tails flying and nostrils wide to the sea wind.

Between this horse and its rider there was a deep trust that had been built up over the years, ever since the *gardien* had cut the animal out of the wild herd and broken him in.

11

Ruefully, the rider recalled the end of the first round of that struggle: the *débrandage*, the kind of rodeo when, for the first time, the horseman had tried to keep his seat on his new mount's back. He had carried the bruises for a long time, but in the end mastery had been his.

Soon it would be the start of a New Year – 1944. The *gardien* let his eyes rove over the peaceful herd of grazing bulls and wondered whether, in the coming summer, the young men of nearby Arles would once again compete in the old Roman arena – once the scene of gory contests between gladiators and wild beasts – to pluck cockades from the bulls' horns.

Last year, for the first time in the long memory of the Camargue, there had been no such event. The Germans had put a stop to all big public gatherings when they had moved in to occupy Vichy France at the end of 1942. The *gardien* had asked his boss, the rancher, why the Germans had done that, and had learned that it was because the British and Americans had invaded North Africa. From then on the rancher had been happy to tell the *gardien* how the war was progressing, pointing out the places where fighting was taking place with the aid of a school atlas.

Then one day the rancher, Etienne Barbut, had taken the *gardien* to one side and, after swearing him to secrecy, had asked him to do a curious thing. If ever the horseman came upon any strangers as he watched over his herd of bulls, he was to report the matter immediately to Barbut. In particular, he was to report any aeroplanes which he spotted flying low down, as though they were about to land at Istres, the airfield that lay close to the shores of the Etang de Berre, the big lake to the east of the Camargue between Arles and Marseille.

For this reason, the *gardien* raised his head, suddenly alert, as his keen ears caught the distant throb of aero-engines. A moment later he saw the aircraft themselves, strung out across the north-western horizon like a gaggle of geese. His eyes widened a little, for he had never before seen so many at the same time. He counted twenty-six as they thundered over his head, four at a time, with two bringing up the rear. The noise of their engines spooked his horse and he had to fight for a few moments to bring the animal under control again; the bulls were already scattering in all directions, but they would have to wait.

The last two aircraft were lower than the others, and the *gardien* could see every detail clearly as they passed overhead, down to the black, white-edged crosses and the oil streaks under the pale blue wings. The aircraft had bulbous noses on which the sun glittered, and slender bodies ending in a kind of double tail. He noted all this carefully, knowing that he would shortly be quizzed by his boss. Most interesting of all, each machine carried what seemed to be two little aeroplanes, one under each wing.

He watched the formation for a while longer as it crossed the coast, losing height steadily and splitting up. The leading aircraft broke away and descended towards Istres, their wheels lowered; the remainder cirled like a flock of pigeons, then more of the big twin-engined machines also dropped away and followed the first down to land.

The *gardien* had seen enough. There would be much work to do later, rounding up the scattered bulls, but first he had to tell his boss about the aeroplanes. Barbut was certain to have seen them too, of course, but the ranch was a good five miles away, too far for him to have seen the little aircraft attached under the wings of the larger ones. That, the *gardien* was sure, was important, although he did not understand why. Neither did he understand the rancher's sudden interest in what was going on at Istres. But then, that was no business of his. He clapped his heels to the horse's flanks and the animal launched almost at once into a supple gallop, sure-footed as it sped across the spongy ground, its hooves kicking up little rainbows of salty spray.

CHAPTER TWO

The six men crawled flat on their bellies across the snowfield, moving forward a few inches at a time. Their white winter-camouflage smocks rendered them all but invisible against the background.

Slowly now, the leader of the six told himself. Slowly. Only another fifty yards to the objective, but don't rush. All the training has paid off. We've come through twenty miles of hostile country to get this far. Only a few more yards. . . .

A machine-gun chattered, the bullets flicking up spurts of snow just a few feet in front of the line of crawling men. They froze, hearts pounding. The burst of fire came again, the second stream of bullets following the path of the first, underlining the fact that it was all over, finished.

Suddenly, the leader of the group wanted desperately to be sick.

'All right,' a voice called. 'You're all dead. Up you get.'

Over on the right, a small group of what had seemed to be boulders suddenly shook themselves free of snow and resolved themselves into men, one of whom cradled a Bren light machine-gun. They advanced to meet the others, who were now rising ruefully to their feet. The man with the Bren stood in front of the leader of the ambushed group and grinned at him.

'Hard luck, Einar,' the man said, a slight Scottish accent betraying his origins. 'But don't look so downhearted. You've come close enough to the target to qualify. The main test was to get across country without being spotted, and this time you

14

managed it very well indeed. Congratulations. Now let's go over to the hut. You've earned your rations.'

Einar, who like the other five in his group was a Norwegian, trudged through the snow towards the hut that had been their objective, shoulder to shoulder with the man carrying the Bren.

'Captain Douglas,' he said, 'does this mean our training is now completed?' The Norwegian spoke excellent English, although a little slowly. He had been a Professor of Physics at Oslo University before the war, and still could not quite comprehend the circumstances which had brought him to this wild and remote part of Scotland on the west coast of Inverness.

The other looked at him, smiling. 'I think it means that the hard part is over, Einar. I can't say I'm sorry, either. After all, we're supposed to be here for a rest.'

Behind Douglas, Sergeant-Major Stan Brough chuckled. Rest – and by that he meant proper rest – was something this particular Special Air Service detachment hadn't known for more than a year. First there had been North Africa, and operations deep behind the enemy lines that had culminated in a hair-raising attack on a German headquarters in Tunisia; then a landing on the island of Pantelleria to blow up Italian gun positions and supply dumps prior to the main Allied invasion; and after that the SAS men had been thrown more or less immediately into the murderous Partisan war in Yugo-slavia, where they had been sent to make contact with Tito, the legendary guerrilla leader.

The wilds of western Inverness were gentle compared to the harsh mountain fastnesses of Yugoslavia, yet in a way Brough had been sorry when the RAF Dakota transport had come to take them away. There was something about that land, and its people, which appealed to him deeply. Maybe he would go back there after the war, if only to see how things had turned out for the people the SAS men and others had gone to help. The same thoughts, he knew, had been foremost in the mind of Callum Douglas, but for the young officer there had been the added attraction of a young Partisan woman called Mila.

Anyway, he told himself, it was all academic. The war might go on for a long time yet, and the odds were stacked heavily against any of them coming through it alive.

Not many of Douglas's original command were left. Some had died in North Africa, others in Yugoslavia. Apart from Douglas and Brough himself, there remained only Liam Conolly, the Irishman, and Trooper Brian Olds, the stolid and dependable ex-farm hand from Norfolk.

Brough looked around at Conolly, who was keeping up a halting conversation with one of the Norwegians in the latter's own language. A born linguist, the Irishman's talent in that direction had got his companions out of a desperate situation on more than one occasion. During the weeks in Inverness he had set himself the goal of learning the basics of Norwegian, and had managed to build up a considerable vocabulary – not that it really mattered to anyone except Conolly, because all the Norwegians spoke English.

Brough shook his head at the memory of some of the irrepressible Irishman's antics during the past year. His native sense of humour had done much to raise their morale in perilous times. He looked habitually untidy, even when wearing his best uniform – a uniform that now sported a sergeant's stripes, which Conolly had accepted only after much protest – and his vivid blue eyes wore a dreamy, faraway expression that belied his talent for killing swiftly and silently with a variety of weapons ranging from commando knives to crossbows. A student of Dublin University, he had been on vacation in Germany when Hitler invaded Poland, escaping by the skin of his teeth on one of the last trains to cross the Dutch border. Brough knew that Conolly had turned down the offer of a commission at least twice.

Brian Olds was a different sort entirely. At this moment he was in the hut up ahead, preparing a meal for the dozen men who had been taking part in the training exercise. It was the farm boy from Norfolk who, in his own quiet, soft-spoken way, had imparted to the Norwegians something of his own uncanny sixth sense; he could look at a stretch of countryside and tell almost at a glance if anything was wrong or out of context in it. His ability to pick out the location of an ambush, a sniper or an enemy patrol simply by observing the movements of birds and listening to their warning calls had proved more than a mere asset; as far as Douglas, Brough and the rest were concerned, it had often been the recipe for survival in a hostile terrain.

Among the others who made up Douglas's ten-man team, two – Troopers Barber and Mitchell – had joined as replacements just before the Pantelleria operation. Barber had created some hostility against himself at first because of his garrulous Cockney nature, but the opposition had disappeared soon after the first demonstration of his ability to move with cat-like stealth over any kind of ground. Mitchell, the signaller, was something of a mystery. He was a Rhodesian, from one of the longest-established settler families, and had the look of the veldt in his grey eyes. He spoke only in monosyllables, as though conserving reserves of apparently inexhaustible energy. He could run up one side of a mountain and down the other, carrying a radio pack, with scarcely an increase in his heartbeat rate.

The other four, Troopers Cowley, Lambert, Sansom and Willings, were newcomers. Cowley and Lambert had transferred to the Special Air Service from the Commandos, and had taken part in the historic attack on St Nazaire in 1942 – the raid that had denied the use of the harbour to the battleship *Tirpitz*. Sansom and Willings had both come from the Royal Engineers, and were demolition experts. All had adapted themselves well to the tough SAS lifestyle.

This, then, was the small band of men who comprised No. 2 Special Raiding Unit, a designation recently bestowed upon them following their activities in Yugoslavia. No. 2 SRU was an offshoot of 'D' Squadron of the 1st Special Air Service Regiment, which – commanded by its founder, the redoubtable Colonel David Stirling – had first won its laurels in North Africa. Stirling was now a prisoner of war, but the organization he had formed continued to flourish and expand.

In the two and a half years of its existence, the Special Air Service had grown from what many senior Army officers had regarded as something of a cowboy outfit into a hard-hitting force which had inflicted damage upon the enemy out of all proportion to its size. The badge of the SAS – Excalibur, the winged sword of King Arthur, surmounting the legend 'Who Dares Wins' – had become an object of fierce pride among those who were qualified to wear it.

Now, in the first days of January 1944, the Special Air Service units which had fought around the shores of the Mediterranean, from North Africa to the Greek Islands, were regrouping and training in readiness for the biggest venture yet: the assault on north-west Europe. No one yet knew when it would come, but all the signs were that it would be soon, within a few months. Britain was being turned into a vast aircraft carrier and a depot for the supplies and troops that were pouring in from the other side of the Atlantic.

Here, in snowbound Inverness, the war seemed very remote. The hut into which the SAS men and the Norwegians tramped was pleasantly warm and filled with the aroma of frying bacon, sizzling away in a large pan which Olds was tending on top of a glowing stove. He turned the rashers, saw that they were ready and scooped them onto a tin plate which he left on the stove to keep warm, replacing the bacon in the pan with a batch of eggs. Minutes later, the men were falling hungrily on the food which he dished up.

Callum Douglas chewed on a piece of bread, made succulent with the last of the bacon fat which he had wiped from his mess tin, and washed down with a mouthful of tea. The influx of sixteen damp bodies into the hut was already making the atmosphere stuffy. They would be spending the night there, and suddenly Douglas felt the need to get as much fresh air as possible before the darkness and the cold confined him to its interior.

Outside, he scrubbed his mess tin with snow before lighting a cigarette. Inhaling deeply, he looked around. The only time he ever smoked was after a meal, when he enjoyed it; any more than that and his mouth felt sour.

He gazed north-westwards across Loch Morar, taking in the spur of land beyond and letting his eyes rest on the dark violet of Skye's rugged hills, rising from the sea in the fading light. Far away, the sun dropped slowly towards the rim of the Hebrides, a cold red ball ensnared in mist.

Douglas shivered slightly, not so much with the cold but at the stark beauty of the scene. Even in the depth of winter the Western Isles, lapped by tendrils of the Gulf Stream, seemed to retain a peculiar warmth all of their own; the snow on them served to soften their contours and make different plays of colour upon them as the light varied, whereas snow merely accentuated the rugged savagery of the highlands that towered to the east.

For once, Douglas noticed, the sea was empty of ships. Normally it was otherwise, for the waters out there were the preserve of the Royal Navy, and nothing other than warships, fishing boats and the necessary island ferries was allowed into them. Because of the heavy naval presence the whole area around the Western Isles was restricted, which suited certain secretive people very well indeed.

Here on the western coast of rugged Inverness, a number of country houses in the vicinity of Arisaig, on the tip of South Morar, had been commandeered early in the war and designated Special Training School Group A. For the past three years, amid this wild and lonely landscape, agents of the Special Operations Executive – the organization responsible for sending its men and women into enemy-occupied Europe to liaise with and train the resistance movements – had been brought to a peak of physical condition and taught how to kill their enemies silently and effectively with whatever weapon was to hand at the time, whether it were a knife, piece of rope, broken bottle or even a rolled-up newspaper. They had also learned how to use pistols and sub-machine-guns, how to jump trains and blow them up, and how to land from small boats on a defended coastline.

Douglas had enjoyed his weeks here, helping to put the SOE

agents through their paces, not least because for him Scotland was home. The rambling house overlooking the River Tay, where he had been born twenty-five years ago, held both fond and bitter memories for him; fond because of the care of his father, who had brought him up, and bitter because he knew his mother only as a blurred memory. His father had destroyed every photograph of her after she had run off with an American rancher, a wealthy Texan who had come to Scotland for the salmon fishing, when Douglas was a very small child.

'Think they'll be all right, sir?'

The voice at his elbow made him start. 'What? Oh, it's you, Stan. What did you say?'

'The Norwegians,' Brough said. 'Do you reckon they'll be up to it?'

Douglas threw his cigarette end into the snow. 'Well, we've taught them all we know, but I've no idea what they will be up against. It's probably for the best that we don't know, but I must confess to being intrigued, especially since most of them appear to be scientists of some sort. They're a nice bunch. I hope it all works out for them.'

Brough began to make another comment, but broke off as a faint, alien sound broke the silence of the hillsides. Both men found the source of the noise almost immediately. Above the shadows that were descending on Loch Morar they made out the cross-shape of an aircraft, turning in its flight and then steadying so that it was nose-on to the two watchers and level with them, as they were several hundred feet up on a hillside. As it drew nearer, Douglas recognized the high wing and heavy, spatted undercarriage of a Westland Lysander. He had seen plenty of them during his time in the desert, and in fact had flown in one during an intelligence operation in Palestine.

The Lysander tilted a wing as it crossed the shore of the Loch, as though the pilot was checking his bearings, then resumed its course.

'Seems to be looking for something,' Brough said, as the aircraft tilted a wing once more.

'Or somebody,' Douglas observed. 'I wonder if it's us? We're the only ones up here at the moment.'

He realized suddenly that the Lysander pilot would have difficulty in spotting them, dressed as they were in their white winter clothing. Quickly delving into his camouflage smock, he extracted the small mirror which he always carried in the breast pocket of his battledress. The sun was not yet fully down and he aimed the mirror at it, making an improvised heliograph.

The Lysander pilot caught sight of the reflected rays and turned towards the flickering light source, flying low over the hut from which some of the others had now emerged, their curiosity aroused by the roar of the engine. They waved, and the gesture was returned by the pilot and his observer, clearly visible in the cockpit.

The pilot turned and flew back towards the hut, throttling back and coming down as low as he dared. As the Lysander passed overhead, its engine idling, the observer tossed a message container from the cockpit. It spiralled down, a red streamer fluttering in its wake, as the pilot gunned the engine again and climbed away to a safer height.

The container landed in the snow some distance away from the group by the hut. Mitchell was nearest to it, and ran through the snow to retrieve it. He brought it to Douglas, who held it aloft and waved at the circling Lysander. The pilot rocked the aircraft wings in response before heading south into the gathering dusk.

Wondering what this was all about, Douglas unfastened the cap of the container and pulled out a rolled-up message form. Around him the others waited expectantly while their officer read it. The message was simple enough.

'Captain Douglas report immediately to telephone box by roadside at head of Glen Beasdale. Transport waiting.' The message ended with a map reference, to make sure that Douglas found the right spot, and the time when it was written. It was signed by a brigadier whom Douglas knew to be on the staff of soe.

Taking Brough on to one side, he said quietly, 'Stan, I've

21

got to go. I haven't a clue what's going on, but this only involves me. Bring in the party as planned, as soon as it's light tomorrow.'

He glanced at the sunset. 'Glen Beasdale,' he muttered to himself. 'That's about three miles away, and all downhill. Well, whoever is waiting won't have to wait long.'

Five minutes later Douglas was ski-ing down the hillside in the twilight, scarf pulled up around his face against the cold breeze. The exercise was to have ended the next day with a cross-country ski run, for which purpose sixteen pairs of skis had been off-loaded at the hut. Douglas was grateful for that now, and for the fact that he knew this bit of territory like the back of his hand. There were few pitfalls, and those that did exist he could avoid with ease, even in the rapidly fading light.

It was almost completely dark by the time he reached the designated spot on the road that led towards Arisaig – the only road, in fact, in this remote part of the British Isles. He unfastened the skis and, resting them across his shoulder, made his way towards the telephone box. There was no sign of the promised transport, but he made up his mind to wait for a few more minutes before ringing up HQ to find out what exactly was going on.

Breaking his self-imposed smoking rule, he lit a cigarette, partly because its glow broke the monotony of the darkness and made him feel a little warmer. He had smoked it down to its last inch when he caught sight of masked headlights approaching from the direction of Arisaig. He moved out into the road to make himself visible.

The vehicle was an Austin 10 light utility car. It drew up a few feet away and the driver got out, a vague shape in the darkness. Douglas could make out little more than the pale blue of a face, topped by a beret. The figure was wearing a greatcoat, its skirt almost reaching the ground.

'Captain Douglas? I'm sorry I'm late. The snow has blown in over the road back there, and I'm afraid I got stuck. Please wait until I turn round before you get in. I might need a push.'

The voice was soft, cultured and unmistakably female.

22

Before Douglas had a chance to say anything, the woman got back into the car and turned it expertly on the narrow, slippery road, causing Douglas to step sharply out of the way. He slid his skis into the back, which was covered by a canvas tilt, then climbed into the passenger seat. As the car moved off, he looked curiously at its driver.

'What are you?' he asked. 'ATS, or something like that?'

He sensed that the woman was smiling in the dark. 'No, captain. I'm a civilian. You can call me Colette, if you like.'

She volunteered no further information about herself, and Douglas was not in the mood for talking, so the two drove on in silence. At length, the car turned left off the winding road and passed between two enormous stone pillars that flanked a gateway. There was no sign of the gate itself, and Douglas suspected that in common with most other ornamental metal structures throughout the British Isles, it had long since been removed and melted down in aid of the war effort.

The car followed a drive for a few hundred yards, negotiated something dark and circular that might have been a pond, then crunched to a halt on gravel in front of a large house. Although familiar with the training area, Douglas had not been here before; in fact, he had had no idea that the place existed.

'Where's this?' he wanted to know, as they got out of the car.

'We call it the Jam Factory', Colette told him. 'The story is that it used to belong to a millionaire who made his fortune out of preserves. It really is a beautiful house, though, as you'll see in a moment.'

They went up a broad flight of steps and Colette rang the bell. A few moments later there was the sound of bolts being drawn, then the big door swung back to reveal a huge foyer with carpeted stairs at its far end. It was lit by a chandelier. No attempt at blackout precautions here, Douglas thought; probably no need of them.

The man who had opened the door was a Military Police sergeant. Douglas saw that he was armed, and that the flap of

23

his holster was unfastened, the butt of a Smith and Wesson ·38 revolver protruding so that the weapon could be quickly drawn.

The MP stepped aside to admit the newcomers. 'Oh, it's you, miss,' he said, nodding at the woman in friendly fashion.

'Good evening, sergeant. This is Captain Douglas. He has been ordered to report to room 20.'

The sergeant made a careful scrutiny of Douglas. 'Evening, sir,' he said politely. 'The order is on my desk, but if I could just see your ID?'

Douglas produced his identity card, which the MP examined at some length before handing it back. 'Thank you, sir. That is all in order. Would you both follow me, please?'

'Just a moment, sergeant,' Douglas said. 'I'd rather like to shed this lot before I go anywhere.' He indicated his winter overalls.

'Right, sir. You can leave it behind my desk over there. No one will walk off with it.

Douglas gratefully stripped off the overalls. As he did so, he was aware that the MP was looking thoughtfully at the ribbons of the Distinguished Service Order and the Military Cross which the SAS officer wore above the left breast pocket of his battledress blouse. The woman, too, took off her greatcoat and beret, which she also left behind the MP's desk.

Douglas gave her an appreciative sidelong glance as the pair of them followed the MP up the stairs. Her shoulder-length black hair was glossy and tied back with a green band; her features, from the side, were somewhat aquiline, with high cheekbones and a curve of the nose that was not unattractive. This, together with a rather dark skin, gave her a Mediterranean look. She wore dark green slacks and a short blouson of the same colour, fastened at the waist with a finely-worked leather belt. The bottoms of her slacks were tucked into fur boots. She was petite, not much over five feet tall. Douglas found himself wondering what her body was like under the clothing, then mentally admonished himself for being a lecherous pig. All the same, he was suddenly uncomfortably conscious that he needed a shave, and that his battledress exuded an odour which was not unlike that of a wet dog.

At the top of the stairs they turned into a broad corridor, their footfalls softened by the thick pile of the carpet. The walls were hung with portraits of stern-looking bewigged men, some of whom wore the tartan. Douglas wondered whether they were the jam millionaire's ancestors, or whether they had come with the house.

The MP halted at a door and knocked. An indistinct command of entry came to them through the oak panelling. He opened the door and snapped to attention, announced the arrival of the two newcomers and then stepped respectfully aside to let them pass.

They entered the room, Douglas following the woman. A man rose from a leather armchair to greet them. He and Douglas looked steadily at one another. It was a half-second, no more, before recognition flashed through the SAS officer's mind – and with it came the certain knowledge that extreme danger must be in the offing.

CHAPTER THREE

Brigadier Sutton Masters extended his right hand as the MP closed the door behind Douglas and Colette.

'Well, Douglas,' he said, 'our last meeting was in a somewhat warmer climate.'

Douglas murmured something by way of response. The last time he had encountered Masters had been nearly six months earlier, in Malta. It had been Masters who, as head of the Balkans Section of SOE, had briefed the SAS officer for the Yugoslavian venture.

There was another man in the room, standing with his back to a crackling log fire. Unlike Masters, who was dressed in civilian clothing, this man wore a uniform – the uniform of a very senior Naval officer, with several rows of medal ribbons making a splash of colour below his left lapel. Masters made the introductions.

'Sir, this is Captain Douglas of the Special Air Service. The young lady you have already met. Douglas, this is Rear-Admiral Sir Richard Westerfield.'

Westerfield was a short man and very lean, obviously getting on in years but still possessing a considerable crop of grey, wavy hair. He regarded Douglas steadily out of eyes that were barely visible amid folds and creases, caused no doubt by the winds that had swept the world's oceans.

'Thank you for coming so promptly, Douglas,' he said. His voice was surprisingly soft, with a hint of the West Country. 'Please sit down, both of you. But first, help yourselves to a drink.' He indicated a tray that stood on a sideboard.

The girl declined, but Douglas poured himself a generous measure of scotch before making himself comfortable in one of the easy chairs that had been placed by the fire. Westerfield came straight to the point.

'Douglas, we have a big problem. It is one that has to be solved very quickly, otherwise enormous damage could be inflicted on certain operations that will be undertaken in the near future.'

He leaned forward and stared at Douglas intently, the heavy gold braid on his forearms reflecting the firelight.

'Early in December,' he continued, 'one of our home-wardbound convoys was subjected to a severe air attack off the Bay of Biscay. Losses were very heavy – about one-third of the ships involved, including an aircraft carrier. This came as a very nasty shock to us, especially as we had begun to get the upper hand in the Atlantic. Now, the thing that made this attack so devastating – and potentially frightening, as far as the future is concerned – is that the Germans used missiles, not bombs or torpedoes.'

'Missiles?' The word was an unfamiliar one, at least when it was mentioned in the context of weaponry. The rear-admiral nodded.

'Yes. Or, if you prefer it, rocket-powered projectiles. Masters, hand Douglas that folder, will you?'

The brigadier obligingly passed over a buff-coloured Ministry file. Douglas opened it, and saw that it contained a selection of photographs.

'Look at them carefully,' Westerfield said, 'and I will explain what they are all about. The first one shows the Italian battleship *Roma* on fire and sinking between Corsica and Sardinia after being attacked by the Luftwaffe. The weapons the Germans used were glider bombs, which we believe were steered to the target by some form of radio guidance. The attack took place in September last year, when the Italians were on their way to Malta to surrender to us after the armistice. Another battleship, the *Italia*, was badly damaged in the

27

same attack. Now look at the next picture.'

Douglas did so. It depicted another warship, this time pictured at close quarters in harbour. Douglas recognized the unmistakable scenery of Valletta in the background. There was a massive hole in the warship's hull.

'That's the battleship HMS *Warspite*,' Westerfield told Douglas. 'She was hit by three glider bombs off Salerno and very severely damaged. She'll be out of commission for months. Now, I want you to close the folder for a minute.'

The rear-admiral got up and resumed his stance in front of the fire. 'Those glider-bombs are very accurate,' he went on. 'There was only one thing in our favour. They had to be launched from close range, a couple of miles or thereabouts. Moreover, the launch aircraft had to fly straight and level over the target while the missile was guided after launch. So, as you may imagine, the Germans took heavy losses from our anti-aircraft fire. Now you can take a look at the third photograph in there.'

It was an aerial shot, showing an area of sea dotted with burning ships.

'Not a pretty sight, is it?' Westerfield said grimly. 'That's the convoy that was attacked off Biscay in December. The photograph was taken by one of the RAF's Sunderlands that went out to look for it. The convoy was heavily escorted, but there wasn't a damned thing the escorts could do to prevent the massacre. It seems the Germans launched their missiles from nearly ten miles away. According to reports, the missiles came in low over the sea at incredible speed – some accounts suggest it must have been over six hundred miles per hour. We have a particularly detailed description from a lookout on board one of the escorting destroyers who tracked a missile with his binoculars; he said that it was leaving a white trail when he first spotted it – presumably the rocket exhaust – but then the trail cut out and the weapon seemed to coast over the final few hundred yards.'

'It makes you wonder what else they've got up their sleeve,' Douglas muttered, trying to imagine the nightmare of terror

28

and suffering that lay behind the frozen, impersonal image of the photograph.

'It does indeed,' Westerfield agreed. 'Incidentally, RAF Intelligence has identified the Luftwaffe unit that carried out the attack. It's called KG100, and it apparently exists to carry out special operations. We think that it was KG100 that led the attack on Coventry back in November 1940. They acted as pathfinders, flying along a radio beam transmitted from a station on the French coast. They've been in Russia for the past couple of years, but now they're back. A few days after the convoy attack, Intelligence pinpointed their base at Cognac, north of Bordeaux. We asked the Americans to obliterate the place with one of their daylight precision attacks. They did it with admirable thoroughness, as you'll see from the fourth picture.'

Douglas stared at what had been an airfield, covered with hundreds of overlapping bomb craters. 'Nice work,' he commented.

'Very,' said Westerfield wryly. 'However, there was only one problem: KG100 wasn't there any more. Over to you, Brigadier.'

Masters coughed and took out a silver cigarette case from his inside pocket. He played with it, unopened, as he spoke.

'Well, it now seems that KG100 has turned up at Istres, in southern France. SOE has received reliable word to that effect from our main resistance contact in the area. This is worrying us a great deal, because from Istres they are in a position to interfere seriously with forthcoming operations in the Mediterranean.'

Masters paused to take out a cigarette and light it. Douglas took the opportunity to ask an obvious question.

'Can't the Americans do to Istres what they did to Cognac, and put the place out of action?'

The brigadier shook his head. 'They tried, and suffered unacceptable losses. The Germans have moved a wing of fighters into Istres. The Americans just couldn't get through. The RAF can't carry out a night attack for fear of causing heavy casualties among French civilians in the surrounding area.' He looked suddenly at Westerfield. 'How much can I tell Douglas, sir?'

The rear-admiral sighed and passed his fingers through his hair, moving away from the fire and sitting down once more. 'All right, Brigadier,' he said. 'I'll take the chance, and the responsibility along with it. Needless to say, Douglas, anything you hear from now on does not go beyond these four walls.'

'You have my assurance on that, sir,' Douglas told him.

'Good. The situation is this. Very soon – before the end of January – an Allied invasion force will go ashore at a location on the west coast of Italy. I'm not going to tell you where, but I can say this: the objective is to take Rome and cut off the enemy forces in southern Italy from those in the north. If we succeed in doing this, we can probably force a complete withdrawal of German forces from Italian territory, leaving the way open for a drive into Austria. Taken alongside other plans, about which I can say absolutely nothing at this stage, it could all add up to the possibility of the war being over this year.'

He smiled, a little wearily. 'Then, Douglas, we can all go home somewhat earlier than we envisage.'

Douglas said nothing. He waited expectantly for whatever was coming next. Westerfield did not keep him waiting for long.

'On the other hand,' he went on, 'unless we can nip this new enemy threat in the bud, and quickly, our plans for a speedy end to the war could face disaster. At this very moment, a large convoy carrying the United States reinforcements and material essential to the success of the proposed landing is assembling in various West African ports. In ten days' time it will pass through the Strait of Gibraltar and head straight for its objective, joining up with other assault ships from North Africa en route.'

Westerfield paused for a moment, as though gathering his thoughts, then said: 'Inevitably, the Germans must know all about the American convoy. Their U-boats tried unsuc-

30

cessfully to attack it in transit, and they have plenty of agents still in West Africa. What they don't know is the objective. Our Intelligence people have been doing their best to lay a false trail in the hope of persuading the enemy that a major landing is about to take place on the French Riviera. The idea is that the Germans, with luck, will remove some of their forces from northern Italy to the Riviera, although as yet we have no reports that they are doing so. Perhaps they think it no longer necessary.'

Douglas looked at Westerfield questioningly. 'Sir?'

'What I mean', the Naval officer went on, 'is that the Germans now probably believe that they can decimate the convoy by use of air power alone as it passes through the Mediterranean. I fear that with these new weapons, they are quite capable of doing so. They have got to be stopped. Back to you, Brigadier.'

'As you have already heard, Douglas,' Masters said quietly, 'we cannot eliminate KG100 by air attack. Clearly, the only way to accomplish it is by an assault from the ground. We want you to take in your SAS team, Douglas, and organize the local Resistance to do exactly that. And it has got to be done within the next ten days – less, for safety's sake.'

Douglas leaned back in his chair and expelled his pent-up breath in a long exhalation.

'Bit of a tall order,' he said. His voice was completely steady, which surprised him; he didn't feel in the least bit steady.

'You have considerable experience in airfield attack techniques,' Masters pointed out. 'In that respect, your record in North Africa was outstanding.'

'Well, sir, with due respect, that was a bit different,' Douglas told him. 'We would pop up out of the desert, hit the target and get out again. We knew the lie of the land, and we had plenty of air reconnaissance to tell us what we were looking for. Besides, the Germans' desert airstrips weren't very heavily defended. At Istres we would be going in blind, not knowing what we would be likely to be up against.'

'Not entirely.' Douglas looked round in surprise; it was the

31

woman who had spoken. Masters looked encouragingly at her.

'Please go on, Colette,' he said. 'But first, Douglas, I should explain that Colette will be going along with you.'

Douglas felt his hackles beginning to rise. 'Now just a minute, sir,' he said truculently. 'For a start, I don't think that any of this is feasible. And even if it were, I don't want any unknown quantities tagging along.'

Masters held up a hand. 'All right, Douglas,' he said sharply, 'just draw in your horns a little and listen to what Colette has to say. She is by no means an unknown quantity, as you will learn. She has our complete support; in fact, she is quite indispensable to this operation.'

There was a lengthy pause before Colette spoke again. She stared at Douglas, and the silence was laden with reproof.

At length she said in an even voice: 'Captain Douglas, I don't think you quite understand. There is a very strong resistance movement in southern France, in some ways stronger than that in the north. In Vichy France we are fighting not only the Germans, but also the Milice, the pro-fascist police, who in many respects are worse than the Gestapo. Let me assure you that you will receive all possible help in your task; in fact, the groundwork is being prepared at this very moment.'

'You seem very sure of yourself,' Douglas interrupted, 'and in any case, I haven't said that I'm going to risk the lives of my men in this crazy venture. I assume' – the question was directed at Masters – 'that you aren't going to *order* us to do this?'

The brigadier shook his head slowly. 'No, Douglas. Of course not. It'll be strictly a job for volunteers.'

Douglas was beginning to feel tired. He lay back in his chair and passed a hand over his eyes.

'Look, gentlemen,' he said, addressing both senior officers, 'I think I would like to sleep on it. First of all, I want a bath and a shave and a change of clothing. That might be a problem, since my kit is over at Group A Headquarters.'

Masters smiled. 'No, it isn't,' he said. 'I had it brought here. There's a room for you. First things first: I suggest that when you have freshened up, you take dinner with Colette. We've quite a nice little mess room here, and there's hardly anybody about just now, so you'll be able to talk privately. Colette can tell you what she knows about the Resistance, and I hope set your mind at rest on a few matters. Then you can give me your answer first thing in the morning. Fair enough?'

'Fair enough, sir. You'll have my answer then.'

'Don't forget, Douglas, that thousands of lives may be in the balance here. I trust you will make the right decision.'

He's putting me well and truly on the spot, Douglas thought. He'll have his answer, all right. But what happens to me if it's the wrong one? And what will happen to me anyway, and especially to my men, if we go?

There was no choice, not really. A suicide mission to save many lives was, perhaps, acceptable. But what if it failed? What if the lives of his men were to be squandered for nothing? He knew that this operation would be unlike anything he had undertaken before. In North Africa, in Yugoslavia, there had been places to hide if the going got rough – places where a few men could hold an army at arm's length if they needed to. But in southern France the enemy were likely to hold all the cards, right from the start. Unless, of course, there were factors of which he was still unaware, secrets which no one had yet seen fit to reveal to him.

First things first, Masters had said. Very well, then. He rose from his chair.

'Will that be all for now, sir?' he asked, directing the question at Masters in a polite tone that by no means matched his mood.

'Yes, Douglas. I will call you in the morning,' Masters said, also getting up. Westerfield rose too, and came forward to take Douglas's hand.

'I don't suppose I shall be seeing you again, Douglas,' he said, and then flashed a quick smile. 'Sorry. I didn't mean that to sound like it probably did sound! What I meant is, I am

33

heading back to the Clyde at once. I have told you all I can. I'd just like to wish you good luck – no matter what your decision may turn out to be.'

At that moment, Douglas made up his mind what he was going to do, come what may. But he had no intention of telling Masters – not just yet.

Colette said that she would show him to his quarters. He followed her up another flight of stairs, and she led him to a door that was recessed into an alcove on the left of the landing at the top.

'Go ahead,' she told him. 'Open it.'

He did so, and gasped in amazement. It was as though he had stepped straight into Jacobean times. The dominant feature of the room was a huge four-poster bed, hung with dark blue drapes that were tied back. Firelight glowed on burnished shields that hung over crossed swords on the wall above the fireplace. The only twentieth-century feature, incongruous and out of place, was an electric table lamp that stood on an eighteenth-century dresser.

'Good Lord!' Douglas exclaimed. 'Who was the last to sleep here – Bonnie Prince Charlie?'

Colette chuckled. 'You might not be far out, at that,' she said. 'He was supposed to have landed at Arisaig, so one of my Scottish friends tells me. Anyway, you might as well make the most of it.'

'And where's your room?' Douglas asked, grinning a deliberately wicked grin.

'Mind your own business,' she told him firmly. 'Now, it's exactly seven o'clock. You've got one hour to sort yourself out, and then I'll come and collect you.'

Someone, Douglas thought a few moments later, was being extremely efficient. His best uniform had been laid out on the bed, together with clean shirt and underwear, and his shoes had been polished until they glittered. Also, to his delight, he discovered that a bath had already been drawn in the adjoining bathroom. His rolled-up winter overalls were on top of his back-pack, which stood in a corner of the room.

Gratefully, he unlaced his boots and peeled off his sweaty battledress. For a few moments he stood naked in the middle of the room, flexing his weary muscles. Then he slid into the bath and luxuriated drowsily for a few minutes before setting to work to soap away the grime that had accumulated during the exercise with the Norwegians. He couldn't help feeling sorry for them, and for his own men, roughing it in the hut up in the hills, yet in an odd sort of way he would rather have been with them. Conolly, he thought with an inward grin, would probably have produced a whisky bottle from somewhere by now, and it would be doing the rounds.

Feeling much refreshed, he had just finished changing into his clean clothing when there was a knock on the door. Colette entered at his summons and smiled at him. 'Good,' she said, 'you're ready. I like punctual people. Very smart, too, if I may say so.'

'Thanks,' Douglas grinned back. 'You don't look so bad yourself.' It was one of his bigger understatements. From where he was standing, she was beautiful. She seemed to have a penchant for green, for she now wore a simply-cut emerald evening gown, fastened at the neck with a little galaxy of stones which, from the way they flashed and sparkled in the firelight, were clearly not synthetic. She wore no lipstick, but a mild touch of rouge accentuated the hue of her complexion.

'Um ... very nice indeed, actually,' Douglas said, rather at a loss for words. 'Well, shall we go and make a dramatic entry into the dining-room?'

The dining-room, he discovered, was on the ground floor. They descended the stairs with Colette's hand resting lightly on his arm, paused a moment at the dining-room door, and saw immediately that the only occupant was a mess waiter, standing stiffly by a serving hatch in starched white jacket. He wore a corporal's chevrons, in gold, on his right arm.

Colette chuckled. 'So much for the dramatic entry,' she said.

The corporal bade them a polite good evening, showed them to a table and placed a menu in front of each of them. The meal was excellent and, apart from game soup, distinctly un-

Scottish; the main course consisted of a brace of small birds which, Douglas found to his surprise, were wood-pigeons, cooked in a deliciously piquant sauce. To finish off there was a custard tart, dusted with nutmeg, followed by fruit and cheese. There was a palatable red wine, too, served from a decanter.

The corporal came to clear the table, and asked them if they would like their coffee where they were, or in the ante-room. Douglas, feeling like a smoke, decided on the ante-room, which was a small and comfortable lounge next door. They settled down in armchairs by the fire; the corporal brought them their coffee and, to Douglas's delight, some cognac, and then discreetly made himself scarce, closing the door quietly behind him with the words, 'Just ring that bell over there, sir, if you want anything.'

'Amazing, this,' Douglas observed. 'I haven't enjoyed a meal as much in years. Can't help being curious about who was behind that serving hatch. One of the faithful old retainers, do you think?'

Colette laughed. 'It's possible. We hardly ever see any of the mess staff. It's all part of the policy, I suppose. The less they know about us the better, even though they might suspect a great deal. By the way, I want to thank you.'

Douglas looked at her in surprise. 'For what?' he asked.

'For not asking any questions during the meal,' she told him. 'I would have hated you to spoil my enjoyment of it. Now you can ask all you want; I'll tell you as much as I can, or as I think you ought to know.'

Douglas offered her a cigarette, which she declined. He lit one himself, then said: 'For a start, I'd like to know who I'm dealing with. Just who are you, and how do you fit into all this?'

She smiled at his blunt manner. 'I already told you, you can call me Colette,' she said. 'As for my employers, it should be obvious to you who they are. And I want you to know this, Captain: I know exactly what I'm talking about. I have been in this game a long time – right from the start, in fact – and I

36

have been in Vichy France twice since it was occupied. Does that surprise you?'

Douglas shook his head. 'Not in the slightest. And my name is Callum, by the way.'

She inclined her head briefly. 'Very well, Callum. Now, my first job is to brief you on what you are likely to encounter in the Vichy zone – assuming you decide to volunteer for this operation, of course. Otherwise, this conversation ends here.' She looked at him questioningly.

'I'm going,' he told her. 'But I think you already know that.'

She nodded. 'Yes, I didn't think you were the kind of man to turn down a challenge, no matter how risky.'

As she began to tell him about conditions in Vichy France, it quickly became apparent to Douglas just how risky this venture was likely to be. Over and over, she stressed the fact that the main threat the SAS team was likely to encounter was the Milice, rather than the occupying German forces. The Milice, she told him, had originated as a semi-chivalrous body of gentlemen anxious to restore France's shattered military honour after the defeat of 1940, but since then it had turned into something much more sinister.

'They are the scum of the jails,' she said vehemently, 'the same sort of would-be gangsters as the thugs Mussolini and Hitler built their movements on. They are Frenchmen who live and work in their home towns and villages, using their local knowledge expertly; that is what makes them so dangerous to our agents. Whereas the ordinary police might be friendly or at least neutral, and the Germans are strangers who might be bluffed, the militiamen are sharp, suspicious characters who are wholeheartedly devoted to the fascist cause. The French SS – oh, yes, Callum, don't look so surprised, there *is* a French SS division – recruits widely from their ranks.'

Douglas listened attentively as Colette went on to tell him about the Maquisards, the Resistance fighters, who had already been betrayed by the Milice.

'The main problem in France.' she explained, 'is that security among the Resistance is virtually nil. It isn't in the French nature to be secretive, and people get arrested simply because they can't keep their mouths shut. That's why I'm pleased we'll be going into the Camargue; people tend to keep themselves pretty much to themselves in that corner of France, which increases our chances. Also, the activities of the Milice are kept under constant surveillance by one very clever – and very successful – Resistance circuit in the area.'

Colette spoke for several more minutes, by which time Douglas had acquired a fair grasp of what he and his men were likely to encounter. When she had finished, she paused for a few moments and looked at him gravely. Then she said, 'There's one thing I have to point out. You will not be able to carry out this operation in uniform. So if anything goes badly wrong and you are captured, you will almost certainly be shot.'

'I've a strong feeling they'd shoot us anyway,' Douglas told her. 'Anyway, you'll be in the same boat, I expect.'

'Perhaps. But the Germans have more refined ways of dealing with captured agents. The lucky ones are shot; the unlucky ones are interrogated by the Gestapo for weeks, perhaps months, before being sent to a concentration camp.'

A flush of anger crept over her face. 'Some day, when this war is over, the deaths of many people will have to be avenged. It will not be easy to sort out the innocent from the guilty among our own people. I sometimes wonder who are the most despicable – those who secretly collaborate with the enemy, or those who come out into the open to side with them.'

Douglas looked at her in curiosity. 'You say "your people,"' he said. 'Are you French?'

She nodded. 'In part, at least. It is a strange and very sad story. Do you wish to hear it?'

'If you want to tell me, I should like that very much,' he said quietly.

'My father was a soldier in the last war,' she told him. 'He was killed at Verdun in 1915, or so my mother believed. We lived in the north then, near Amiens. I was only a few months old.'

The statement took Douglas by surprise, for it meant that

38

Colette was older than she looked.

'For a time my mother was inconsolable,' she went on. 'Then, in the early months of 1918, she met an English officer, a good man. He married her, and brought us back to England with him. We were happy – until the day my mother discovered that my real father was still alive.'

'Good God!' Douglas interjected. 'What happened?'

'I don't know, exactly,' Colette admitted. 'It wasn't until years later, after my stepfather died of tuberculosis, that I found out anything about it. All I knew was that during the intervening years a profound change had come over my mother, something neither my stepfather nor I could understand. She never told him, of course.'

She paused and drew a deep breath, betraying how painful the story was to tell. Nevertheless, she went on with it.

'It seems that my true father was blown up by a shell. They found him on the battlefield, stripped naked by the blast, alive but suffering from severe head injuries. He knew nothing of where he was, or who he was. It was only after he had spent some years recuperating in a succession of hospitals that the authorities managed to piece together his identity, and notify my mother through their various channels.'

'Did you ever meet him?' Douglas asked gently. Again, the woman nodded.

'Yes, but only once. We travelled to France not long before this war broke out, not knowing what to expect. I, of course, had no recollection of my father, but my mother found a total stranger – a man with no memory of anyone or anything beyond that day in 1915. It was hopeless, right from the start. They parted, having talked politely to each other for a while, and never saw one another again. He is still in France, and quite a wealthy man, in his own way.'

There was a long pause, and then Douglas asked: 'And your mother?'

For a while, he thought that she was not going to answer his question. When her reply finally did come, it was barely audible.

'She was killed in the raid on Coventry in November 1940. So you see, Callum, I have a personal vendetta against Kampfgruppe 100.'

CHAPTER FOUR

Royal Air Force Station Tempsford was an odd sort of place. Douglas knew nothing about it, apart from the fact that it was some kind of jumping-off point for clandestine operations into Occupied Europe.

On the face of it, Tempsford was hardly an ideal location for work of this kind, for the A1 Great North Road lay on one side of it and the main London–Edinburgh railway line on the other. Yet its very openness may have helped to preserve its secret identity, for few railway passengers can have taken much notice of the collection of decrepit-looking and obviously out of date aircraft they spotted from the windows of their carriages as they passed by. The villagers of nearby Tempsford eventually guessed, inevitably, that something unusual was going on, but there were never any recorded instances of careless talk.

Evidence that Tempsford's secret was very well kept lay in the fact that although the Germans knew that the RAF's special duties aircraft were operating from a base some thirty miles north of London, they only once came near to finding it. That had happened one night in the spring of 1943, when a lone German bomber flew over the airfield and dropped a string of flares across it. The anti-aircraft defences kept silent, not wishing to betray the well-camouflaged objective. The bomber circled for some time but the crew apparently saw nothing and flew away, dropping their bombs on a nearby nursery garden.

Douglas and his team disembarked from the Albemarle

transport aircraft that had brought them from Prestwick in mid-morning. The sky was clear, the sun glittering on a crisp carpet of snow, which, after a mild December, now, lay over Tempsford. They were met by an Army major, muffled in his greatcoat against the keen January wind. Douglas saw at once that the Albemarle had dropped them on the opposite side of the airfield to the main site; as soon as they were clear of the aircraft, the pilot taxied away round the perimeter track in the direction of the distant hangars.

The major led Douglas, Colette and the others along a footpath that ended at the door of a solid, brick-built barn. Inside it was comfortably furnished with armchairs, a table and a sofa; covering the whole of one wall there was a map of France and the Low Countries. A tea urn stood on the table, with piles of cups nearby.

'Make yourselves comfortable,' the major told them, 'and help yourselves to some tea. A van will be over a little later on with some hot food, and afterwards we will issue weapons and clothing. There will be a lengthy briefing in the course of the afternoon.'

'About the weapons, sir,' Douglas said. 'I specifically requested MP-40s and ammunition. Have they arrived?'

The major nodded. 'Yes, Douglas, they have. Some priority was attached to their delivery, in fact. They'll be brought over from the armoury this afternoon.'

Douglas felt satisfied. On every operation he and his men had so far undertaken, they had chosen the German MP-40 machine pistol as the optimum weapon, not least because the 9-mm ammunition it used could be readily obtained when operating behind enemy lines. It was also simple to break down into its component parts, a useful feature when it came to concealment. Brigadier Masters had tentatively suggested that they take the recently-designed Sten gun along with them, but Douglas had declined; he had fired one and found it to be highly inaccurate, as well as prone to jamming. Stan Brough, in his blunt Yorkshire fashion, had endorsed Douglas's feelings.

'Bloody Sten? Couldn't hit a barn door with one if you were

sat on the latch,' had been his comment.

The major turned to leave. Douglas had noticed a motor cycle outside; that must be his transport. He turned as he was about to open the door.

'Just one thing,' he said. 'This is to be your home until you leave tonight, and I must ask you not to set foot outside the door until then. There's a lavatory through that door at the back, inside a small yard, with washing facilities. I'm afraid it's a bit primitive, but it's the best we can do. Sorry for the inconvenience, miss.'

'Don't worry about it, Major,' she smiled. 'I've been in worse places.' The major looked slightly embarrassed and left, carefully closing the door behind him. They heard his motor cycle start up and chug away.

'Well, this is fun,' said Conolly, crossing to the solitary window and rubbing some condensation from it with his sleeve. 'What a dump.' He peered moodily out over the snow-covered airfield.

Douglas sat lost in thought while Conolly produced a pack of cards and persuaded some of the others to join him in a game of poker. Colette reclined in an armchair, reading from a slim, leather-bound volume she had brought with her.

Douglas felt more than the usual sense of unease about the forthcoming operation. So much depended on the woman; what if she were to become separated from them during the drop? Only she knew where the contact was to be made. He didn't like it at all. He had a strong gut feeling of helplessness, brought on by the knowledge that in this matter – for the time being at least – he was not master of his own destiny.

Some time later lunch arrived in a NAAFI van and was served up by two cheerful middle-aged women who, Douglas suspected, were more than they seemed to be. The food was basic – vegetable soup followed by sausages and mash – but they ate it with relish nonetheless, seated around the stove that stood in the middle of the barn.

'Nice touch, this is,' commented Barber, the cockney. 'Good

old bangers an' mash. Won't be much of that where we're going.'

Douglas shot him a warning glance, but the women who had served the meal had not heard him, or pretended they hadn't. Colette smiled at him. 'You can have mine, if you like,' she told him. 'Not my favourite food, I'm afraid. Anyway, I'm not hungry.'

Barber took the plate from her with a mumbled thank you that changed to a shout of protest as Conolly pinched one of his sausages.

The two women collected the empty plates and disappeared. The men resumed their game of cards and Colette went back to her book. Douglas fidgeted and wondered how much longer they were going to have to wait. Inactivity chafed on his nerves.

It came as a relief when an RAF truck drew up outside. Douglas, looking through the window, saw some stores being unloaded from the rear of the vehicle. The Army major stepped down from the cab, followed by an RAF officer. The latter approached the barn, opened the door, nodded cheerfully to the occupants then stood aside to admit a relay of airmen, carrying assorted boxes and bundles of clothing which they placed on the floor. Finally, they brought in what Douglas had been waiting for: the MP-40 machine-pistols, together with a case of ammunition.

The men appeared totally unconcerned, as though their activity was routine stuff – which, Douglas told himself, it probably was. He could guess that whatever aircraft were hidden in the hangars on the other side of the airfield plied a regular trade into the heart of Occupied Europe, carrying their cargoes of gallant agents – men and women alike – who were fighting their own secret war against Nazi tyranny and who faced, at best, a quick death if they were captured, and at worst a lingering one at the hands of Gestapo torturers.

The airmen departed without a word, not sparing anyone a glance. Douglas heard the RAF officer tell them to come back in an hour. Then he re-entered the barn, followed by the major.

Douglas saw that he had the rank of wing commander. The major introduced him, after a fashion.

'This officer is the wing commander (flying) on this station,' he said. 'His name, of course, is irrelevant. He is here to brief you on tonight's operation.'

The wing commander peeled off his greatcoat, revealing an impressive array of medal ribbons under his pilot's brevet, and draped it over the back of a chair. He was not very old, probably not yet out of his twenties, but his relative youth was partly camouflaged by an enormous handlebar moustache. His eyes were old, though; the eyes of a man who had seen too many of his friends set out on operations, never to come back.

He stood with his back to the wall map and surveyed the gathering for a few moments before speaking. His voice was clear and slightly high-pitched. He wished them good after-noon, and a reciprocating murmur went around the room. They looked at him expectantly.

'I'm afraid I have some very bad news for you,' he said with a slight smile that rather gave the lie to his words. 'The weather forecast for southern France tonight is not good; lots of low cloud. So that means we can't parachute you in. Sorry to disappoint you.'

Douglas could sense the relief among his colleagues. All had been through the parachute course at Ringway, but few of them had made an operational drop; none of them had been looking forward to it, especially at night.

'However,' the wing commander continued, 'there are other ways and means. One of the aircraft types we operate here is the Lockheed Hudson; for the benefit of the uninitiated, that's a twin-engined aeroplane kindly supplied by our American friends. Coastal Command used a lot of them earlier in the war, and we've got a few of their cast-offs for long-range trips where we need to land a number of passengers. Usually we take a maximum of eight, but this time we're going to stretch a point and take all eleven of you. After all, I don't suppose the young lady weighs very much. One of the advantages of the Hudson for this sort of job is that it lands in a very short distance.'

The wing commander paused briefly, fiddling with the button of his tunic left breast pocket. Douglas noticed that two fingers of his right hand were missing.

'Be under no illusion that this is going to be an easy trip. It won't be. Under different circumstances, with more time available, I would have recommended a different course of action – flying you out to Gibraltar, and then landing you on the Riviera from the sea. As it is, you are faced with a four-hour flight, almost all of it over enemy territory, and at the end of it we've got to land you on a strip about the size of a cricket field. Fortunately, our crews are the best in the business; they'll get you there. After that, it's up to you and the reception committee. We've already sent a coded signal to them to advise them of the change in plan.'

He turned to the wall map of France and tapped it with his index finger. 'The landing zone is here,' he told them, 'northeast of Vauvert, between Nîmes and Arles. It's about two miles from the main road that runs to the coast, and passes Istres. It's one of our regular landing-grounds, and there are no Germans in the immediate area – at least, not as far as we know.'

The wing commander finished his briefing and then handed over to the major, who first of all indicated the bundles of clothing. Bending down, he picked one up, untied the string band that was holding it together, and shook it out. They saw that it was a black, one-piece garment. The major explained its purpose.

'These are a new type of overalls designed especially for SOE operatives engaged in sabotage and other covert work at night. They are waterproof and flame resistant, and are fitted with a hood so that the wearer can render himself virtually invisible against a dark background.'

'Good job there's no snow where we're going,' someone chuckled. The major shot a frosty look at someone behind Douglas.

46

'Quite. Now, if I may continue. As you will see, the overalls contain plenty of pockets, including a built-in sheath here on the right leg for the standard one-pound Sheffield dagger. What you store in the other pockets is up to you; I know that you like your own private arsenals. As far as explosives and detonators are concerned, these have already been air-dropped to the Maquis in your operating area. When you change into your overalls, please bundle up your uniforms and leave them here; they will be looked after and forwarded to you upon your return.'

'Optimist', somebody murmured.

The major ignored the remark, then said: 'As this is not a normal SOE operation, you will not be carrying the standard issue equipment used by our people in the field. However, we can let you have something that may be of use to you in the unhappy event that you are taken prisoner.'

He delved into a carton and produced a handful of small, transparent packages, each one marked with a different colour, and held them up in turn. 'These are pills to resist fatigue,' he told them, 'and these produce a high fever and every symptom of typhoid. They have, on occasion, been known to get people out of a tight fix by persuading the Germans to transfer them from a prison cell to hospital, from which escape is obviously much simpler. And finally, we have these.'

He opened one of the little packages and a glass capsule rolled into his palm. He held it out so that they could all see it.

'Concentrated arsenic,' he said mildly. 'Inside the capsule it's quite harmless; you can keep it in your mouth and even swallow it. But break it between your teeth and you're dead in less than a minute – about forty-five seconds is the average for a normal, healthy person. It's not a pleasant way to go, but preferable to some of the alternatives, should you fall into enemy hands.'

Douglas resolved to have nothing to do with that particular form of self-execution. The rest of them, it seemed, felt the same way, for when it came to distributing the pills, they all left the arsenic capsules alone. All except for Colette, who picked up three or four of them.

Douglas looked sideways at her. 'You'll only need one,' he said. She gave a short laugh.

'Oh, it's not for me. The arsenic might come in handy for dropping into somebody's coffee, though.'

Douglas was forced to agree with her. Changing his mind, he picked up a couple of the tablets himself and stowed them away in a pocket of his overalls.

Take-off was scheduled for 20.00 hours. That would get them to the landing zone shortly after midnight GMT, well inside the hours of curfew imposed by the German occupation forces. In this way, there was less risk of the clandestine landing being seen by casual eyes.

The Hudson's mid-upper gun turret had been removed, presumably to save weight and add to the aircraft's range. Canvas 'bucket' seats had been fitted on either side of the fuselage interior. The Hudson carried a crew of three: pilot, navigator and wireless operator, who would normally have doubled up as air gunner if there had been any guns for him to sit behind. Douglas saw that the navigator had his left hand and wrist in plaster, and inquired about the injury; the man told him cheerfully that he had fallen off a beam in the Mess bar at Tempsford during a prank a few days earlier.

The Hudson's passengers made themselves as comfortable as they could as the pilot taxied out and revved his engines at the end of the runway. Douglas's black overalls felt stiff and smelt of oil – something to do with the waterproofing, he told himself..It made him feel slightly sick, and he hoped he would get over it. His MP-40 was lashed securely to a metal strut beside him.

The pilot gunned the engines to full power and the Hudson began to move. After a few seconds the rumble of its under-carriage ceased as it lifted away from the runway, turning as it climbed on course.

For Douglas, the next four hours were the most nightmarish he had ever spent. The Hudson was flying in cloud for most of the time, lurching and bumping as it encountered turbulence.

Nothing but inky darkness was visible through the small window next to his seat. Warm air was coming out of the aircraft's heating system somewhere near his backside, and after a while he began to sweat. He had taken a bath that morning – they all had – and had shaved an hour or so before take-off, but the heat began to make him feel scruffy and queasy.

They had eaten a substantial meal earlier that evening, and some of the passengers were beginning to regret it. From behind Douglas came the sound of someone retching into a paper bag, and the nauseating stench of vomit drifted through the aircraft, starting a chain reaction. For a while Douglas tried hard to breathe through his mouth, then he too succumbed.

The wireless operator came round with some coffee, which made the sufferers feel much better, and collected the noxious paper bags.

'I'll drop 'em down the flare chute,' he yelled to Douglas above the roar of the engines. 'We're well inside enemy territory now – might give some Jerry a nasty surprise!'

Douglas grinned weakly. His eyes were well accustomed to the darkened interior of the aircraft now, and he could easily see the figures of his companions, slumped in their various attitudes of misery.

Some time later the airman came back and roused Douglas from a heavy sleep.

'Skipper wants to know if you'd like to come up front. We'll be starting our descent soon so that the navigator can pick up some landmarks.'

Gratefully, Douglas followed the wireless operator on to the flight deck. The airman took his seat behind the pilot, who half-turned and motioned him into the second pilot's seat. The navigator was already down in the Perspex nose, ready to get his bearings when the Hudson broke cloud.

The wireless operator tapped Douglas on the shoulder and handed him a flying helmet, complete with face-mask and microphone. Douglas put it on and the airman plugged the microphone lead into a nearby socket.

'Can you hear me OK?' The pilot's voice sounded in Douglas's earphones. 'Just put the mask across your face and flick that little switch at the end when you want to talk. Don't forget to switch it off again when you've finished talking, though, or it makes unpleasant noises over the intercom.'

'I can hear you fine,' Douglas told the anonymous pilot. 'Have we far to go?'

'About fifty minutes. Sorry about the bumpy ride, but at least the cloud gave us cover from any fighters that happened to be around. Bit of flak as we crossed the coast; quite close, really. Must have been radar-directed. Did you see it?'

Douglas had to admit that he hadn't. Nothing, as far as he knew, had interrupted the pitch darkness outside.

Suddenly, the Hudson popped out of the cloud base. 'Thank God for that,' the pilot said fervently. 'Two thousand feet – a bit higher than the Met people led us to believe. You could have been parachuted in, after all. Oh, well, this is what I'm paid to do, I suppose. Any idea where we are yet, Taff?'

'Still looking,' the navigator answered from his position in the nose. He sounded worried. 'I hope we haven't drifted too far east of our track, or we'll be into all the high ground. Can't see a damned thing except what's directly below.'

'We ought to be somewhere near Montauban,' the pilot told Douglas. 'We've been flying more or less due south to avoid letting down into the high ground of the Massif Central,' he explained. 'Mind you, with the cloud base as high as it is, we could have taken a more direct route and avoided most of it. But there it is. Can you see anything out of your side?'

Douglas peered out of the window on his side of the cockpit. Strangely enough, although there was cloud above the aircraft, and no moon to afford even a haze of light through its layer, he found that he could pick out some detail against the dark shadow of the ground; the faint ribbons of waterways made patterns in the gloom.

He was still looking when the navigator's voice came over the intercom.

'Hold on, skipper, I think I've got something.' There came

a few seconds' pause, and then: 'Yes, I'm certain now. That's the Garonne up ahead. We're a few miles west of track.'

The navigator made a few rapid calculations, then ordered the pilot to turn on to a heading of zero nine eight degrees. 'That'll take us between Montauban and Toulouse,' he announced, 'and put us on track for the landing zone. We've lost a little time, but we've got a good tailwind now. We should make our ETA all right.'

The pilot tilted the Hudson's left wing and swung round on to the new heading. As they flew on, the navigator kept up a running commentary on the landmarks that came up under the nose. Douglas noticed that there did not seem to be an effective blackout; lights flickered in towns and villages, making the navigator's task easier. He remarked on it to the pilot, and also on the fact that they hadn't seen a single searchlight.

'The searchlight and flak belts are concentrated in the north,' the pilot informed him, 'stretching in arcs from the Channel and North Sea coasts right back into Germany. There's hardly anything in the way of air defences this far south – lucky for us.'

They flew between Castres and Albi, scene of terrible religious persecution in medieval times, and then crossed a hilly region dotted with lakes that showed up in the valleys as patches of dark gun-metal. At length, the navigator announced that they would be passing five miles north of Montpellier in eight minutes' time. Their target area was approaching fast.

'I'm going to ask you to go back to your seat now,' the pilot said to Douglas. 'The navigator will be coming up out of the nose as soon as we spot the LZ.'

'Right. I'll go and alert the others. Thanks for the ride.'

Douglas climbed out of the right-hand seat, passed his helmet to the wireless operator and went back into the fuselage. He told the others that they would be landing in about ten minutes, and there was a flurry of activity as they checked their weapons and equipment. If the reception committee turned out to be hostile, they were determined to give a good account of themselves.

In the nose of the Hudson, the navigator picked out a faint 'V' of roads, just visible in the darkness. The left-hand fork led to Nîmes, the right-hand one to Arles. He had done all he could. Somewhere, just up ahead – unless things had gone badly wrong – the Maquisards would be waiting to detect the sound of the aircraft's engines before lighting a rudimentary flarepath. He scrambled out of the nose position and climbed into the seat recently vacated by Douglas.

'Nice work, Taff,' the pilot said quietly. The navigator grunted. He didn't think that he had done anything special.

They circled, looking for the elusive pinpricks of light that would show them the position of the landing ground. The blackness below remained unbroken.

'Bit bloody grim, this is,' the pilot remarked. 'Could have done with a moon. Surely they must have heard us by now? I hope there hasn't been a cock-up. Can't go on swanning round the sky for much longer.'

The navigator said nothing. He was concentrating on scanning the ground as carefully as he knew how. After a few more tense minutes, his persistence was rewarded by the sight of a red light ahead and off to the right. It flickered on and off in a series of dots and dashes.

'Recognition signal, skipper,' the navigator said urgently. 'Two o'clock. We're just about on top of it.'

'OK. Got it.' The pilot turned the Hudson towards the flickering signal and flashed the aircraft's navigation lights in response. A few moments later, two parallel lines of flowing dots came to life. The flarepath seemed ridiculously small. This landing, the pilot knew, was going to need every ounce of his accumulated skill. The wireless operator, returning from a quick trip to the main cabin, assured him that the passengers were firmly strapped in.

'Right. Here we go, then.' Gently, the pilot eased the Hudson round until it was in line with the flarepath, landing into wind. They already knew which direction the wind was coming from, for the navigator had been checking it throughout the flight, but the pilot saw with satisfaction that the reception committee had placed an additional flare at the upwind end of the strip. He suspected, although he could not see, that it also marked the boundary of the field, which was useful to know.

He lowered the undercarriage and flaps and throttled back gradually, allowing the Hudson to sink towards the flarepath but ready to open the throttles again instantly if some obstacle loomed up out of the darkness. But the reception committee had done its work well and the approach to land was faultless and trouble-free, the flarepath seeming to expand and meet the Hudson as it sank through the last fifty feet. The pilot checked its sink rate with a gentle backward pressure on the stick and, with the flares rushing past the wingtips, allowed it to stall on to the ground.

The undercarriage hit the earth with a thud that rattled the entire aircraft. The Hudson bounced a little way into the air and the pilot fought to keep the wings level as it settled again. This time it stayed down, the pilot ruddering to keep it straight and applying the brakes cautiously. Mud or water, possibly both, splattered against the fuselage.

In the cabin, Douglas held his breath and looked out of the window apprehensively, seeing the flares rush past. Then the Hudson began to slow down and finally stopped altogether, its engines ticking over. A collective sigh sounded in the cabin as its occupants expelled their pent-up breath.

The wireless operator came back into the cabin and unlatched the main fuselage door. Douglas and his companions had already unfastened their seat belts. The SAS officer had no need to tell the others what to do. Led by him they tumbled out into the night, machine-pistols at the ready, and deployed in a line that extended outwards from the aircraft, flinging themselves prone on the ground.

Even at this moment of potential danger, the thought ran through Douglas's mind that the moist earth and the clean night air had never smelt so sweet.

They lay there, M P-40s cocked, and waited. Apart from the rhythmic beat of the Hudson's still-idling motors, there was no sound in the night. Then Douglas sensed, rather than saw, shadowy movement beyond the aircraft's tail. He settled the butt of the MP-40 into his shoulder and prepared to open fire.

CHAPTER FIVE

'Montfort!'

The word came unexpectedly out of the darkness. It was Colette, lying next to Douglas, who provided the response.

'Montségur!'

She levered herself upright and looked down at Douglas. 'It's all right,' she told him. 'They're friends.' The SAS men also rose and followed Colette to meet the reception committee. One of the latter, his features invisible, began to say a few words, only to have them drowned by the sudden roar of the Hudson's engines. Douglas winced; the aircraft was making enough racket to wake the entire neighbourhood.

The roar died away to its previous idling rumble. A moment later, the fuselage hatch opened and the wireless operator jumped down.

'I say,' he said urgently, 'we seem to be stuck. The skipper wants to taxi back down the strip so that he can take off into wind, or we won't get off at all. Can you give us a shove?'

Colette quickly explained to the Maquis reception committee what had happened. Without a word, the Frenchmen – there were eight or nine of them – clustered around the Hudson alongside the SAS newcomers and laid willing hands on the aircraft at spots indicated by the wireless operator, who now jumped back on board. The pilot gunned the engines again, showering his helpers with mud as they pushed with all their strength.

After a couple of minutes, it was apparent that the Hudson

was not going to come free. The wheels were sinking deeper into the waterlogged ground. At length, the pilot shut down the engines altogether and climbed down from the aircraft.

'It's no use,' he told them dejectedly. 'She's bogged, and no mistake. We've already made enough noise to wake the dead. Wouldn't surprise me if the Germans or the Vichy cops are on their way here now.'

Colette spoke again to the reception committee, some of whom immediately turned and ran off into the night.

'They've gone to get some shovels,' she said. 'They always bring some with them in case it's necessary to bury parachutes or other equipment. We'll have a go at digging you out.'

The pilot sounded relieved. 'That's fine. But I don't think I can risk giving it much more than an hour – say ninety minutes at the outside. If we haven't got clear of the mud at the end of that time I shall have to set fire to the aircraft to prevent it from falling into enemy hands.'

A few minutes later, the Frenchmen returned with the shovels and a couple of picks, which they immediately applied to the mushy ground in an effort to dig shallow, sloping trenches to front and rear of the Hudson's main undercarriage. It was difficult work in the darkness, especially as the trenches rapidly began to fill up with water. After a while the pilot, afraid that one of the picks might pierce a tyre, called a halt.

'I'm afraid it's hopeless,' he said. 'Look – she's sinking even deeper. The bottom of the fuselage is just about resting on the ground. I'm just going to have to burn her,' he ended mournfully.

Suddenly, a warning shout sent the group around the Hudson scattering to retrieve their weapons. One of the Frenchmen, who had been acting as lookout, thought he had seen some movement beyond the flarepath. He was right; in the flickering light of the flares, some figures approached cautiously. The lookout, gun at the ready, ordered them to put up their hands and come closer. Whoever they were, Douglas thought, it was apparent that they were not Germans.

They turned out to be men from a nearby village. Alerted

by the roar of the Hudson's engines, they had defied the local curfew to see what was going on. Colette spoke to them in low tones; after a couple of minutes they hurried off.

'That's a stroke of luck,' the woman told Douglas and the pilot. 'They've gone to fetch some horses and oxen. They say they'll be back inside an hour.'

She had a hurried consultation with the Frenchman who appeared to be in charge of the reception committee, then turned back to address Douglas.

'All this is making us late,' she said, 'but I don't see what we can do. The Maquisards are determined to stay here until the Hudson is either airborne or set on fire; in the latter case, the last thing they want is for the RAF crew to roam around the countryside until they are taken prisoner, which would almost inevitably happen. If things do go wrong, they'll be taken with us. And since we can't go a step further without the help of the Maquisards, we'll just have to wait with them. There's no alternative.'

Douglas nodded. 'Right. But first of all I suggest you get somebody to extinguish the flares, at least until those villagers come back. I don't think there'll be much flying under the cloud tonight, but we can't risk being spotted. Also, I'm going to deploy my men around the aircraft and well away from it. If the Germans do turn up, at least we can give them a hot reception.'

Out there in the darkness, lying a few yards next to Olds, Douglas tried vainly to relax as he waited for the return of the villagers. Every small night sound made his nerves jump, and his eyes began to ache and smart with the effort of peering into the shadows. The minutes, ticked off by the luminous hands of his wrist watch, crawled around the dial with the speed of a lame snail.

Olds, with his keen hearing, was the first to detect the jingle of harness, and alerted Douglas with a warning hiss. Suddenly, by the edge of the field, a light flared, followed by another and another.

'Oh, my God,' Douglas groaned. 'They've lit torches! What

the hell do they think this is – bonfire night?'

'It will be, if we don't get that 'plane out of the clarts,' said Olds practically. 'Anyway, they must be pretty certain there are no Jerries around.'

They stood up and watched the approaching cavalcade. It seemed almost that the whole village had turned out to help. The two groups of Frenchmen, villagers and Maquisards, greeted each other with much hand-shaking and back-slapping. The throng milled around the stranded Hudson for a while, then sorted itself out into some kind of order; a team of draught horses was harnessed to the undercarriage legs, and the work of freeing the aircraft began once more.

Despite the combined efforts of men and animals, it was another thirty minutes before the Hudson finally came clear of the mud with a gigantic sucking sound.

The crew lost no time in boarding the aircraft, the Maquisards scattering to relight the flarepath as the horses were unharnessed. The Hudson's engines coughed into life and the aircraft began to move, the pilot turning cautiously and starting his taxi run to the downwind end of the flarepath. Douglas glanced at the sky, and saw with some apprehension that the cloud layer was beginning to break up, increasing the risk of the flarepath being spotted by any aircraft that chanced to be in the area. It would also increase the hazards the RAF crew might have to face on the long flight home.

A group of Frenchmen completed their task of filling in the holes which the Hudson's wheels had dug into the airstrip, and ran clear as the pilot revved up his engines to full power. He released the brakes and the aircraft began to gather speed, its momentum slowed by the weight of the thrown-up mud that caked it. Half way down the strip, with the tailwheel only just clear of the ground, the pilot felt with sickening certainty that he was not going to make it. The Hudson's take-off speed was ninety miles per hour, and with the flare that marked the far boundary rushing closer, the airspeed indicator showed only fifty.

Then the miracle happened. The Hudson hit a bump and

lurched into the air. Somehow the pilot kept it flying, teetering on the edge of a stall, and flew between two trees at the far end of the field. There was a crunch as its wingtip sliced through some branches, and then it was climbing away into the night.

Back on the field, Colette came to stand beside Douglas as the drone of the Hudson's engines faded.

'I hope they make it,' she said softly. 'They are very brave men.'

'I hope we all make it, but we won't unless we get a move on,' Douglas reminded her. 'What's next?'

'I've had a word with the Maquis leader,' she told him. 'We're being taken to a farm a couple of miles away in the first instance. After that I don't know. It seems we have to meet somebody. We are completely in their hands, for the time being at least, so we will just have to go along with them. I'm afraid that one or two of them are a bit suspicious of you and your men. You're something out of the ordinary, so I expect there will be questions they want to ask.'

The Maquisards, having seen the villagers safely on their way home, led the way to their destination along a track that wound its way through sparse woodland. They marched in single file, carefully spaced out, keeping the SAS men in the middle.

Presently, the trees thinned out and gave way to an expanse of scrub – the maquis from which the French Resistance movement had taken its name. As they went on, Douglas noted that one of the Frenchmen took care to fall in close beside him. The man reeked of stale sweat and garlic. Douglas took an instinctive dislike to him, even though he had no doubt that the Frenchman was simply obeying orders and would, without hesitation, slit the SAS officer's throat if the need arose.

They crossed a narrow dirt road and, after a few more minutes, a cluster of low buildings loomed out of the darkness. The group made straight for the biggest one and halted outside while the Maquis leader went forward and rapped sharply on the door. He called something out in a low voice, there was a response from inside, then a rasping sound as bolts were drawn. The door swung open, revealing an aged woman in a long black dress silhouetted against the light of a lantern. She waved them inside and snapped something at the French leader in a shrill tone.

Colette, who was in front of Douglas, gave a chuckle and half turned. 'Roughly translated, the old woman wants to know where the hell we've been,' she explained. 'She says that she's been up half the night cooking for us, and now the food is nearly ruined.'

They filed quickly into the building and one of the Frenchmen closed and bolted the door behind them. Douglas saw that they were inside what appeared to be a timber barn or storehouse of some sort, with a high roof and beams running from wall to wall. A lantern hung from one of the beams, and sacking had been hung over the windows to prevent its light being seen from outside. The interior of the barn was acrid with smoke that curled from an ancient stove.

'They've done us proud,' Colette whispered to Douglas. 'Look at the table.'

Douglas did so. A long table, with benches on either side, had been carefully laid with best crockery and embroidered napkins. There were even real crystal glasses.

'This must have been collected from every home in the village,' Colette said. 'It's the kind of stuff that only appears when there is a grand occasion, such as a wedding, baptism or funeral.'

'Well, I hope it isn't our funeral they have in mind,' Douglas remarked sceptically. 'I've just noticed that most of our French friends seem to have disappeared.'

'I shouldn't worry about that,' she told him. 'I overheard their leader tell them to mount guard around the village. It might be to stop us getting out as much as to prevent the Germans getting in, though,' she admitted.

Only two of the Maquisards remained in the barn, and Douglas now had his first chance to study them closely. The first man was their leader. He was short, with a sallow face framed in dark stubble and thin, rather cruel lips. A black beret was tilted forward over his brow. Douglas saw that he was armed to the teeth with an assortment of weapons, including a Sten gun, a pistol and a long combat knife.

The other Frenchman was the individual who had marched alongside Douglas. In contrast to his leader, he was tall and lanky, with brutal, simian features and close-set eyes under beetling brows. The ends of a sparse moustache dangled past the sides of his mouth. He stood leaning against the wall by the door, casually picking his fingernails with the tip of a stiletto, staring at Douglas with an unwavering, hostile gaze.

Douglas smiled engagingly at him and murmured to Colette, 'Who is the chap with the charmless stare?'

'Do not worry, my friend. That is just Jean-Pierre's way. He means no harm.'

The words came from the Resistance leader, and took both Douglas and Colette by surprise. Neither had realized until now that the man spoke English. Douglas felt somewhat relieved; it was going to make things a good deal easier.

The Frenchman, Douglas discovered, called himself Raoul. He invited the SAS men and Colette to be seated at the table, and the old woman served them with generous helpings of an omelette from two pans on the stove. Raoul fetched some bread, and made the sign of the cross on the back of each loaf as he cut it. Then he poured some wine into the glasses from a large pitcher and stood back from the table, watching them as they ate and drank.

The old woman hovered over them throughout the meal. She seemed to have taken a particular fancy to Conolly, who whispered something in her ear, causing her to cackle shrilly. Apart from that, few words were spoken until the dishes were cleared away. Then Raoul indicated a pile of blankets in a corner of the barn.

'Sleep now,' he told them. 'In the morning I will take you to where you have to go. You, Mademoiselle, will spend the night with my mother.' He inclined his head in the direction of the old woman. Douglas felt a niggle of suspicion.

'Are you sure that's all right?' he asked Colette.

She smiled. 'Perfectly. There's no need to worry. Besides, it means I won't have to share that bucket with you.' She pointed to a rusty object by the wall. There was a small pile of torn-up paper beside it. The Maquisards, it appeared, had thought of everything.

'No one is to leave the barn until we come for you,' Raoul warned. 'Now, sleep well. Tomorrow there may be danger.'

He went out, followed by Colette and the old woman. The brutal-looking Jean-Pierre showed no sign of leaving, so Douglas rose from the bench and made to go towards him. Conolly placed a restraining hand on his arm.

'Leave it to me, sir, if you don't mind. I know his type. Besides, I speak some French.'

Douglas nodded. Conolly ambled over and stood a foot or two in front of the Frenchman, then said something in a low tone, smiling amiably as he did so. Jean-Pierre turned and spat on the floor, then resumed his original stance by the door.

The Irishman spoke to him again, a little more sharply. This time, the Frenchman flattened himself against the wall, knees slightly bent. His right hand came up to the level of his chest, the stiletto blade pointing towards Conolly. The latter smiled again and spread out his hands, as though in apology, and turned away as though to rejoin the others. A sardonic smile of triumph crept over the Frenchman's dull-witted face.

The next instant he was on the ground, writhing in agony and clutching at his genitals, where Conolly's kick had just landed. Strangled noises came from him. The Irishman bent down, scooped up the fallen stiletto, and tossed it to Barber, who caught it deftly. With the other hand he seized Jean-Pierre by the jacket and hauled him upright. Opening the door, he tossed the Frenchman out into the night, then shot the bolts into place.

'Nasty piece of work, that,' Conolly said. 'I don't think we'll have any more trouble from him, though. He was just testing us, to see how far he could go.'

'Well, now he knows,' Douglas remarked. 'I hope you're right about him not causing any more trouble. By the way, something has just struck me. Barns usually have bolts on the outside of the door. Here it's the other way round.

Conolly shrugged. 'Probably the Resistance hold meetings here, and it's a safeguard against uninvited visitors,' he said. 'Anyway, it means nobody can creep in on us in the night.'

'Nevertheless, you and I will keep watch while the others get their heads down,' Douglas told him. 'The more I see of this set-up, the less I like it. Stan, I'll wake you in a couple of hours.'

Brough nodded and handed out the blankets to the others. Soon, all except Douglas and Conolly were asleep. Douglas, worried by his feeling of unease, paced restlessly around the room and wished that he could see outside. On more than one occasion he was tempted to open the door and take a look, but decided against such a move. In due course, he and Conolly were relieved by Brough and Sansom, but even then he found it impossible to sleep properly. After a while he lapsed into a fitful doze and awoke unrefreshed at dawn, with a foul taste in his mouth.

A pounding on the door roused them all and they tumbled out of their blankets, reaching for the MP-40s. They kept the doorway covered as Lambert drew the bolts on Douglas's signal and swung the door open. Pale daylight flooded into the barn and Raoul stood on the threshold.

'You can come out now,' he told Douglas. 'There is no danger as yet. We have time to eat.'

They filed out of the barn, looking around them in curiosity, seeing their surroundings clearly for the first time since their arrival in France. The barn in which they had spent the night, they now saw, stood on the edge of a small village, a cluster of half a dozen cottages with white limestone walls and red roofs. The village lay amid fertile, green countryside, with a range of hills climbing on the northern skyline.

The old woman came out of one of the cottages, tottering under the weight of a huge and steaming tureen. She placed it

63

on the ground and then went back indoors, returning with a pile of bowls and some sticks of bread which she distributed among the SAS men. Unbidden, they dipped their bowls into the tureen, which was filled with hot soup. It had a vegetable flavour which Douglas could not quite place, and was slightly spiced. He tore off a hunk of bread and dipped it into the liquid.

'Where is everyone?' he asked Raoul. The Frenchman waved a hand towards the cottages. 'Indoors,' he said. 'We thought it better that you were seen by nobody but myself and my mother. Jean-Pierre and the other Maquisards have gone back to the hills. This is a place of old women and little children.' He paused and then said, very seriously, 'You should not have antagonized Jean-Pierre. Despite what I said earlier, he can be a dangerous enemy. But then, you are not likely to meet him again.'

'Just as well,' Douglas muttered. 'But where's Colette?'

'Gone,' the Frenchman told him, and smiled thinly. 'Don't look so alarmed – she will be back before too long. Then my task will be over, and I can get back to my real work.'

Douglas looked at him, puzzled. 'Which is?' he wanted to know.

'Why, making life as uncomfortable as possible for the Germans, of course,' Raoul told him. 'That has been my main occupation for some time now.'

Douglas was still perplexed. He set down his soup bowl and asked, ' But who are you? Your English is far too good for you to be what you seem.'

For the first time, Raoul allowed his face to relax into a grin. 'Maybe that's because I'm not French, Captain Douglas. I'm French-Canadian. Got taken prisoner at Dieppe, escaped, and made my way south to the Vichy Zone. Thought I'd head for Marseilles and hop a ship for Algiers. Then the good guys invaded North Africa, and that was that. So I decided to devote my war effort to helping out in these parts. The Maquis could use my military experience. They're a good bunch, but piss poor at organizing anything.'

'Well, I'll be damned!' Douglas exploded. 'Why the blazes didn't you tell me this in the first place?' He frowned suddenly. 'But the old woman – you called her your mother.'

Raoul nodded. 'Yes. I've been calling her that for months now – kind of got used to it. She took me in and fed me when I wandered into this place, and put me in touch with all the right people. She wanted me to call her mother. I think I'm a sort of replacement for her real son, who went off and joined the Foreign Legion and got his head blown off fighting the Arabs.'

Douglas shook his head. 'Amazing. But you haven't answered my original question. Why didn't you let me know who you were right away?'

'Because I wanted to know more about you,' Raoul said. 'This is my territory, and I don't like to be in the dark about anything that goes on it. Now that I know a bit more about why you are here, I'll have some of my men keep an eye on you – just in case you run into trouble.'

'Colette told you why we are here?' Douglas asked quietly.

'Not everything, but enough,' the other replied. 'Certainly enough for me to realize that if your plans don't succeed, it will be some time longer before I see Quebec again.'

Douglas had not the heart to tell Raoul that he had no plans, at least not yet. So much depended on Colette, and the next contact along the Resistance line.

Their breakfast over, they collected their weapons and equipment and, on Raoul's advice, took shelter in a small copse that stood a few hundred yards away from the village to await Colette's return. By this time, the clouds that had shrouded southern France during the previous night had broken up almost completely, and the sun rose higher in a watery blue sky. The breeze from the Mediterranean was cool, but not unpleasantly so. Olds glanced up at a blackbird, singing lustily in a treetop, sniffed the air and announced confidently that it would rain before the day was many hours older.

Douglas deployed his men along the edge of the copse

that faced the village. Now that the soldiers had gone, those villagers who remained came out of the cottages and busied themselves with their morning tasks of feeding livestock and collecting eggs; no one so much as glanced in the direction of the trees. It was all a bit unreal; here they were, in the heart of enemy territory, overlooking a peaceful village where the only sign of the war was the absence of menfolk. This area, Douglas told himself, must be completely safe, otherwise the Germans and the Milice would have been asking awkward questions as to the men's whereabouts.

Olds had been right about the rain. Before midday the clouds gathered again and the rain came, torrents of it, heavy but warm, streaming from a leaden sky. A mist of droplets drifted across the grassy plain that ran southwards from the village.

Just after noon, Sansom, who was keeping watch at the left-hand end of the line, raised the alarm. Douglas ran across to him, carefully keeping under cover of the trees, and asked what it was the trooper had seen. Sansom pointed towards the south, and the SAS officer made out a vague white blur of movement through the rain.

After a few seconds, the blur resolved itself into a small herd of white horses. There were only two riders, who appeared to be driving the rest. They headed towards the village and halted beside the farm. One of the riders got down and spoke to Raoul, who had appeared from one of the houses. Douglas counted twelve horses in all, and reached the obvious conclusion.

'Unless I'm much mistaken,' he said to Sansom, 'that's our transport.' Fortunately, after his own experiences in Yugoslavia, where the Partisans had made much use of horses, he had insisted on every man in his section learning to ride on the grounds that it might come in handy. It certainly looked as though his foresight was going to come in handy now.

The rider who had spoken to Raoul remounted and cantered towards the copse. It was Colette, now wearing a broad-brimmed cowboy-type hat and a poncho. Both streamed with water. She dismounted again and unslung a pair of large saddle-bags from the horse's back.

'There are some hats and ponchos in these,' she explained. 'Put them on. You'll be less conspicuous that way. Then follow me down to the village.' Jumping astride the horse once more, she galloped off without another word.

Douglas and the others did as they were told. Back at the village, Colette and the other rider were busily shortening the long reins they had been using to control their respective teams of horses as they drove them across the plain; it was a technique, Colette explained, that had been in use in the Camargue since the days of the Romans.

Colette made no attempt to introduce the other rider, who remained a little aloof from the rest of the party as they mounted up. The horses were spirited, but controllable. Conolly, Douglas noticed, was more at ease than any of them; the look that crossed his face as he caressed the neck of his mount was almost one of exultation.

As they trotted out of the village, destination unknown, Douglas turned in the saddle and gave a brief salute to Raoul, who raised an arm in return. Douglas wondered if they would ever meet again. The odds, he thought, were stacked heavily against it.

CHAPTER SIX

General Horst von Falkenberg stepped down from the Volkswagen 82 Kubelwagen – the Wehrmacht's equivalent of the famous American jeep – and swore fluently as his highly-polished boots sank into four inches of mud. He turned and glared at the driver, a young Luftwaffe corporal.

'Idiot!' he snarled. 'Couldn't you have picked a drier spot?'

The corporal reddened and muttered an apology. The general's criticism was hardly fair, for the entire surface of the field had been turned into a quagmire by the heavy rain.

The Kubelwagen was accompanied by a two-ton Opel Blitz half-track. Twenty heavily armed soldiers jumped down from the back of it and, spurred by the harsh commands of an NCO, spread out across the field, forming a protective cordon around the general. Two more men stepped out of the cab, in which the driver remained. The taller of the two wore a long greatcoat that bore the insignia of a Luftwaffe colonel; the other was dressed in civilian clothing but might just as well have been in uniform, for the thigh-length black leather coat and the dark, broad-brimmed felt hat were the characteristic of the Gestapo.

The two men approached von Falkenberg and the Luftwaffe officer saluted. He was beginning to feel warm in his greatcoat, for the rain had ceased some time ago and the sun had come out again.

Colonel Karl Preuss, officer commanding Kampfgruppe 100, was beginning to wish that he had never set eyes on von Falkenberg. Despite his First World War decorations, the man had become a typical staff officer, haughty and overbearing, straight from the plush and relatively secure offices of the Reich Air Ministry in Berlin. He had, Preuss suspected, authorized a trip to Istres for himself as much to sample the wine and food of Provence as to see how the new weapon worked, which was ostensibly the reason behind his visit.

Von Falkenberg had been at Istres for less than forty-eight hours, and in that time he had never been off Preuss's back. He wanted to fly, to see the new weapon in action for himself. Preuss had spent hours trying to convince him that the weather was unsuitable, that there was little in the way of a worthwhile target, that the weapons were in short supply anyway, and existing stocks had to be carefully husbanded for the coming big operation. It was all useless. Von Falkenberg wanted to fly, and see one of the weapons launched at something. Preuss had resigned himself to the fact that once the general had made his trip, he might then go back to Germany and leave everybody in peace.

Then this little business had cropped up, just to complicate matters even further. A couple of nights ago, a local militiaman had received a report that an aeroplane had come down somewhere in this area. The German authorities had been informed, and had sent out a Fieseler Storch observation aircraft to make a low-level search. Its crew had not found any downed aeroplane, but they had sighted what appeared to be pronounced tyre-tracks in a long field. It was a little unfortunate, Preuss thought, that von Falkenberg had got wind of the affair; the general had insisted on seeing for himself, and so here they were, in company with a weasel-faced little runt from the Gestapo.

'Where?' the general demanded curtly. The Gestapo man regarded him through slitted eyes, and there was a long pause before he answered. Even generals did not use that tone of voice to the Gestapo these days, and fail to have their names entered in a little book for future attention.

He pointed with a black-gloved hand. 'Over there, I believe, Herr General.' There was a slight and rather sinister emphasis on the title. The Gestapo man's tone did not go unnoticed by von Falkenberg, who chose to ignore it.

They trudged through the mud to the spot indicated. The twin set of tyre tracks was easy to see. The party followed them, noting a spot where they appeared to sink deeper into the ground. The general turned to Preuss.

'Your opinion, Colonel?' he demanded.

Preuss peered at the marks. 'Aircraft tyres, most definitely, Herr General,' he said. 'Quite a large aircraft, obviously, and heavily-laden on landing, judging by the depth of the ruts. Also,' he added professionally, 'I would say that the tyres were of American make. The tread has quite a distinctive pattern. Possibly a c-47, or Dakota, as the British call it.' In this he was wrong, but his analysis was close enough.

'Sir!' The shout came from the Luftwaffe corporal, the general's driver, who had been following the party at a respectful distance. He hurried across and stood rigidly before von Falkenberg, saluting crisply. The Gestapo man saw that the salute was of the standard Wehrmacht type, rather than the version pioneered by the Führer. That, too, would be noted.

Anxious to redeem himself for his earlier failure to deposit the general in a dry patch, the corporal said, 'Herr General, I humbly beg to report that there are more tracks over there. They are not as easy to see as these.'

The general nodded. 'Good, Lehnert. Well done. We shall take a look.'

He strode across the field, followed by his entourage. The Gestapo man found that he was almost forced to trot to match the strides of the general and Colonel Preuss, and fumed inwardly at this indignity. Something would have to be done, he told himself, to teach these Luftwaffe upstarts a lesson.

The second set of tyre marks ran parallel to the first, some distance away and on slightly drier ground. The general and Preuss spent several minutes inspecting them, and also some curious circular marks spaced at intervals alongside. At length, Preuss gave his opinion.

'It is quite clear what happened here,' he announced. 'An

70

aircraft, quite heavily laden, landed here and disgorged a cargo of some sort. At the end of its landing run it became bogged down, was extricated, and then took off along this line here, where the ground is a little drier. These circular marks seem to have been made by oil drums – used, no doubt, to form a flarepath.'

The general looked at him with some amusement. He had reached the same fairly obvious conclusion some time ago.

'Quite,' he said drily. 'But what we need to know, Preuss, is what, or who, was off-loaded from the aircraft.' He turned suddenly to the Gestapo man.

'Where is the nearest village?'

Thrown by the sudden question, the Gestapo man pulled a map from his pocket and consulted it. 'About a mile in that direction, Herr General,' he said, pointing towards the west. Von Falkenberg nodded.

'Very well. Then I suggest you take these troops and make a thorough investigation. Find out what the villagers know. I am sure there are methods you can use, if they prove reluctant to talk.'

The Gestapo man glared at him, but said nothing. Von Falkenberg turned to Preuss and said: 'You can come back to Istres with me in the Kubelwagen, Preuss. I hardly think we shall need an escort. The weather is clearing nicely; I wish to fly this afternoon.' He turned on his heel and strode back to the car, the driver running ahead and Preuss following, swearing quietly to himself.

Some hours later, a twin-engined Dornier 217 bomber made its ungainly way around the perimeter track at Istres. The aircraft was heavily laden; in addition to a substantial load of fuel, it carried a pair of stub-winged missiles under its wings, each one weighing a ton.

The Dornier turned on to the runway. In the cockpit, Colonel Preuss opened up the engines to full power and the aircraft began to move, laboriously at first, held back by the weight it carried. The tail came up but the pilot continued to hold the Dornier down on the runway, adding a few extra knots to the normal take-off speed for safety. Then it was airborne and climbing away ponderously, its undercarriage coming up as it entered a steady climb, circling over Istres before settling down on a south-westerly heading.

Heavily conscious of the presence of General von Falkenberg just behind him, occupying the radio operator's seat, Karl Preuss chewed on an unlit cigar and allowed his thoughts to wander. Despite the authorization signed personally by von Falkenberg, everything about this flight was highly irregular and ran counter to the orders Preuss had received from the Luftwaffe High Command. Those orders had stated, quite specifically, that the new weapons were not to be used again until the chance came to mount a major attack. The factory that produced them had been heavily bombed, and it would be some time before production picked up once more. The missile stocks at Istres were all that existed.

The trouble was, Preuss thought, that von Falkenberg outranked the officer who had signed the order. There wasn't much he, a mere group commander, could do about it. Inwardly, as he flew on, the pilot cursed everything; the war, von Falkenberg, the improvement in the weather which had made this flight possible, the reconnaissance report of a large enemy freighter west of Sardinia, the freighter that was now their target. Preuss hoped fervently that the ship was still beyond the range of the Spitfire squadrons that had recently moved into Corsica.

Hampered by the drag of its missiles, the Dornier was making a bare 180 miles per hour. At this rate, it would be over an hour before the bomber reached the target area. To help pass the time, and also to relieve some of the tension that gripped the back of his neck, Preuss decided to make some small talk. Over the intercom, he spoke to his observer, Sergeant Rainer Becher, who was crouched at his station in the bomber's glazed nose. Much depended on Becher's skill, for he was responsible for guiding the missiles. The other crew members, navigator and flight engineer, had their respective positions behind the pilot. At action stations, each crew member manned an MG131 machine-gun, while the pilot controlled a forward-firing cannon mounted in the nose and operated by a trigger on his control column.

'How is Fritz, Becher?'

In the nose of the aircraft, Becher grinned. Fritz was the code-name for the missiles suspended under the Dornier's wings. They were fitted with a special system that piped hot air to them in flight from the aircraft's engines – an essential precaution, otherwise their complex mechanisms would almost certainly freeze at altitude. Becher decided to say something for the benefit of the general, who was also listening on the intercom.

'Fine, sir. Warmer than we are, I'll bet. And with any luck a lot warmer than a great many Tommy sailors will be before long.'

Preuss decided that small talk might not be such a good idea after all. Highly professional military man though he was, he did not relish the prospect of condemning men to death by drowning. That fate had brushed its wing darkly over his own face on more than one occasion, when he had struggled back home in a damaged aircraft following some anti-shipping operation. But this was total war, and at last his group had been given an effective method of waging it – as the previous month's operation against the convoy off the Bay of Biscay had shown.

They called the new weapon Fritz-z, although its proper designation was PC1400z. It was developed from the earlier Fritz-x glider bomb which had been used successfully against Allied warships in 1943. Fritz-z's liquid-fuel rocket motor boosted it to a speed of over 600 miles per hour, which made it virtually unstoppable. It was guided to its target by radio control, the operator steering it by means of a small joystick mounted on the side wall of the cockpit.

That was Rainer Becher's job, and he was good at it. During missile trials in the Baltic he had hit the target nine times out of ten, and he was just as good on actual operations. The other operators in the group were not quite up to his standard, but good enough.

The minutes dragged by. At last the navigator, who had been poring over his charts, taking drift sightings and calculating where the enemy ship ought to be if it had not changed its course and speed, called Preuss over the intercom.

'Maintain heading and airspeed, pilot. Target should be thirty miles ahead in Sector Dora Friedrich 4022.'

Preuss acknowledged briefly and consulted his own map, singling out the reference mentioned by the navigator. DF4022: that would put the ship about one hundred and twenty miles west of Sardinia's Cap Spartivento. So far they had not sighted any other vessels, which was all to the good; the presence of a lone Dornier, heading southwards across the Mediterranean, was bound to excite suspicion and send the RAF's long-range Beaufighters scurrying into the air from some Algerian airfield.

So far, Preuss had kept the Dornier at low altitude to avoid detection by the British radar that had recently been installed on Corsica. Now, with the target area coming up, he took the bomber in a climb to 12,000 feet, the optimum height for launching the missiles. The pilot peered ahead, scanning the rather murky horizon; there was quite a lot of haze, but visibility was not too bad. It should not prove difficult to detect a sizeable vessel, assuming that it, and they, were in the right place at the right time.

In the Dornier's glasshouse nose, Rainer Becher was fussing over his control panel, making last-minute adjustments to the missile guidance system and his high-magnification tracking sight. At length, he reported to the pilot that all was ready. The Dornier droned on, and General von Falkenberg, who had been listening in silence to the crew's chatter over the intercom, suddenly became impatient. He began to bombard the navigator with questions, demanding to know if the man was sure his calculations were correct. Karl Preuss, inwardly furious but striving to keep his voice calm, intervened on behalf of the navigator before he could reply.

'Herr General, as captain of this aircraft I must remind you that you are a passenger on an operational mission, and as such I must respectfully ask you not to interfere with my crew members in the performance of their duties.'

There was a highly charged silence, punctuated only by a strangled sound over the intercom, presumably from von Falkenberg. Mercifully, before the general had time to launch into his anticipated tirade, Becher's excited yell sounded from the nose.

'Target ahead, two o'clock! On the horizon!'

Sure enough, there it was – or rather there they were, for there were two ships instead of the expected one. They were elongated streaks against the lighter horizon, one larger than the other. Preuss called the crew to action stations, turned the nose of the Dornier to the right until the ships were directly ahead, and settled himself firmly in his seat as he began the run-in. He had already decided to launch from six miles to make doubly certain of a hit, having deduced that the smaller of the two ships was most likely an escorting destroyer and that the aircraft would be well outside the range of its armament.

The sea crept under the bomber's wings, and the tension in the cockpit increased as the two ships grew larger. In the nose, Becher, his eye already glued to the tracking sight, began the count-down. 'Number one missile ready and armed. Stand by. Thirty seconds ... twenty ... fifteen ... ten ... five ... launch!'

Preuss, who was in control of the launch, pressed a switch on his control column and at once throttled back. The Dornier, freed of the missile's weight, gave a sudden leap and Preuss rapidly re-trimmed the aircraft to compensate for the asymmetric effect of the remaining weapon that hung under the starboard wing.

The released Fritz-z, still travelling at the original speed of the bomber, sped ahead of its parent aircraft. Becher pressed a button on his control panel and there was a vivid flash of flame as the missile's rocket booster ignited. At the same time, a brilliant flare also lit up in the weapon's tail. Becher picked

75

this up and centred it in the cross-hairs of his sight, then moved his control stick until the flare was superimposed on the outline of the target – the bigger of the two vessels.

Mentally, he counted off the seconds to the missile's objective. Fritz was travelling very fast now. The glare of its rocket exhaust was suddenly cut off as the fuel burned itself out, but that did not matter; the weapon had more than sufficient forward speed to carry it over the last few hundred yards. Becher, handling the control stick with sensitive fingers, kept his eye glued to the sight and centred the tracking flare on the grey, magnified hull of the freighter, just above the waterline.

Travelling at more than 600 miles per hour, the missile's armoured warhead sliced through the freighter's hull as though it were tissue paper and its thousand-pound charge exploded in the engine room with terrifying force, killing everyone there instantly and rupturing the boilers. From the Dornier, the German crew saw a great column of smoke and steam erupt from the stricken ship, which immediately broke in half and began to sink. General von Falkenberg, who had come up to stand behind the pilot's seat, slapped Preuss on the shoulder, their earlier exchange of words apparently forgotten, and clapped the pilot on the shoulder in an uncharacteristic display of excitement.

'Good, Preuss!' he shouted. 'Very good indeed! Now for the other ship!'

The destroyer had turned towards the approaching Dornier and was heading towards it at full speed, shrouded in smoke as it opened fire with its forward armament. Shell-bursts spattered the sky ineffectually a long way ahead of the aircraft. Becher completed his second count-down and the other Fritz-z dropped away, spearing towards the warship at the head of a trail of flame and smoke.

This time, Becher kept the flare centred on the destroyer's bridge. He did not miss. The missile flashed over the ship's forward four-inch gun turret and blasted the superstructure into a shambles, killing the captain and his executive officers.

The destroyer maintained her speed and her guns kept firing, but she was leaderless now, her nerve-centre destroyed. She might survive to limp back to port, but she would be out of action for months, possibly for the duration of the war.

Preuss swung the Dornier round and pushed the nose down to gain speed, anxious to get clear of the area before Allied fighters showed up. He had no doubt that they would, for the ships must have been signalling frantically for air cover.

'That has shown them that the Mediterranean is not yet an Anglo-American pond!' von Falkenberg cried. 'You will all be decorated for this – I shall see to it in person!'

And no doubt you'll be at the top of the awards list, thought Preuss wryly. Nevertheless, he was glad that the general had enjoyed his trip; it would make life a lot easier back at Istres. Maybe von Falkenberg would now go away and leave everybody in peace.

Preuss suddenly felt tired and washed out. He wished fervently that the war was over and that he could go back to his pre-war job as an airline pilot with Lufthansa, the German civil airline. That had been fun, especially the long-range mail flights to America that were just getting started when the war brought a stop to them. The pilot did not think about the lives he and Becher had just ended; he had long ago ceased to give that sort of thing any thought. What grieved him now, in these first weeks of 1944, was that no matter how hard he and his comrades fought on, Germany had lost the war. No matter how many Allied soldiers and sailors they killed, there would be others to take their place. And all Germany had were growing numbers of old men and boys to take the place of the troops who were being massacred and frozen in Russia, the human sacrifices of men such as von Falkenberg and the madman at the helm.

For a wild, impulsive instant, Preuss had an almost uncontrollable urge to send the Dornier plunging into the sea. It passed, but afterwards he found himself trembling slightly and sweating. Now, added to the fear that was a natural reaction to the constant strain of combat flying, was another, even greater fear: the fear of himself.

How long, he asked himself as the Dornier slid down the sky towards Istres, could he go on – how long could any of them go on?

CHAPTER SEVEN

The rain had stopped, but the illusion of warmth it had brought to the Camargue was now dispelled by the breath of the mistral, blowing icily down the valley of the Rhône. It rattled the shuttered windows of the ranch-house where Douglas and his men now sheltered. The ranch stood midway between the village of Albaron and the Rhône, beyond which lay the SAS commandos' objective: Istres airfield.

Douglas, with the aid of sketch-maps compiled by the rancher, Etienne Barbut, was trying to work out how to carry out a reconnaissance of the target. He saw at once that it was not going to be easy. If they went overland from their present location, they would have to cross the broad, fast-flowing Rhône and then cross two main roads to get near the airfield boundary, and as far as Douglas could make out there was very little in the way of cover; anyone seen prowling around in the vicinity of the field would certainly be arrested, for Istres had recently been placed under heavy guard.

His opinion was challenged by Barbut, who explained that, south of Arles, the river opened out considerably and as a consequence the speed of its flow lessened. However, it was half a mile wide at its narrowest, and although there were no German or Milice patrols on this side – mainly because there were no proper roads running through the Camargue – there were plenty on the other, and it would be difficult to cross the river unseen.

Douglas pondered on this, and frowned as he considered

the possible alternatives. His finger traced the course of a railway line that ran from Arles to Miramas and then branched off to Port-de-Bouc, on the coast. The important point was that it appeared to run past the eastern boundary of the target airfield.

'What about this?' the SAS officer wanted to know. 'Wouldn't it be possible to see most of what is going on at Istres from a train?'

Barbut smiled, and once again spoke through the medium of Colette, who was acting as interpreter. Douglas noticed that the elderly rancher seemed to get on very well with Colette; there was almost a bond of affection between them.

'That is exactly how some of these sketches were compiled, my friend. The driver of one of the locomotives on this line is sympathetic. But one has to have a special permit to travel as a passenger, and passes are always checked by the Germans and the Milice. You would be spotted immediately.' Barbut suddenly looked upset. 'Be assured, my friend, that the sketches are as accurate as we can make them. They show where every aircraft is dispersed, the location of the buildings, the dump where the weapons are stored. We have done our best.'

Douglas smiled at him. 'I don't doubt that for a moment,' he said. 'What I am looking for is a way in – and, what is just as important, a way out again once the job has been done. Come to that, I haven't yet worked out how we are going to put a spanner in the works. A lot depends on your Maquisards.'

Between them, they had worked out a tentative plan of action. While the local Maquis launched a strong attack on the airfield perimeter at a point yet to be determined, the SAS men would go in elsewhere. Their main objective would be the weapons dump, but they would also try and destroy as many of KG100's aircraft as possible.

There was much groundwork still to be done, and when the action came it would have to be carried out quickly and with accurate timing. When the Allied convoy that was bound for Italy was about to pass through the Strait of Gibraltar, Etienne Barbut, the local Resistance leader, would receive a coded signal from London. After that, the SAS and the Maquis would have about four hours in which to move into position and launch their respective attacks. That, Douglas calculated, was the time it would take the Germans to receive intelligence of the convoy's movements and to plan their assault on it. In his own mind, he was convinced that the Germans would try to hit the convoy as it passed Gibraltar in order to create maximum confusion, rather than wait until the ships were in the Mediterranean and sailing along the North African coast, where they would probably have fighter protection.

But he did not like second-hand information. He had to see the layout at Istres for himself.

Looking at the sketches again, and comparing them with a map of the local terrain, he was struck by the possibility that it might be possible to approach the airfield from the south. He could follow the Rhône southwards to the coast, cross the mouth of the river somehow and come inland by Port-de-Bouc. That way there would only be one road to cross before he was within sight of Istres.

Through Colette, he told Etienne Barbut of his scheme, mentally calculating the time still available. He alone knew that the convoy was due to enter the Strait of Gibraltar on 19 January, although he did not know the time; it was now the fourteenth. He made up his mind that there was no time to spare for shuttling back and forth across the Rhône; once he and his men were on the east bank of the river they would have to stay there and lie low until it was time to carry out the attack. He asked Barbut if he thought the plan was feasible. The rancher shook his head slowly.

'It is possible, of course,' he said, with Colette translating. 'But it will mean extra organization. For example, you will need a boat to get you across the river mouth, for there is no bridge. Then we shall have to find somewhere safe for you to hide, provide you with food, and arrange for our men to make contact with you there. Then there is the problem of the message from London: how will I be able to get it to you?'

Barbut's brow furrowed for a moment or two, then he

brightened and gave a broad grin.

'Of course, my friend! What could be simpler? I shall come with you? Your signaller here' – he waved at Mitchell – 'has a radio set which is the same type as mine, and works on the same frequencies. I regret that I cannot entrust you with the code, as that would put too many lives at risk if you were to be captured, but if I come with you I can listen out for the message and send the acknowledgement. Besides, I could do with a little excitement! Is it agreed, then?'

Douglas opened his mouth to protest, but Colette placed a warning hand on his arm.

'I think that would be a very good idea,' she said. 'Monsieur Barbut will be a great asset. He knows the area thoroughly. Above all, he is trusted. No one will question him if he is challenged by the Milice,' She smiled. 'In fact, I think they are a little afraid of him. The Camargue is a strange, sometimes eerie place. Those who live outside do not consider it wise to cross the paths of people who belong to these marshes.'

Listening to the mistral moaning its dirge outside, Douglas could well believe some of the superstitions. There were, after all, enough of them among his own Gaelic race. After some hesitation, he agreed to take the rancher along.

They spent some time discussing the equipment they would need. Barbut's cellar contained a sizeable collection of the necessary tools for espionage and sabotage, air-dropped by the RAF during the past months; as well as the radio transceiver he had mentioned, there were daggers, miniature cameras, a selection of German and British igniters, delayed-action pencil detonators, plastic explosives and silent pistols. Douglas distributed the explosives and detonators among his team, and also some German 9-mm ammunition which the Resistance had 'liberated' from the enemy.

Suddenly, as he was completing this task, there came a sharp rapping on the door. Immediately, the SAS men scattered and flattened themselves against the wall on either side, ready for instant action and out of sight of whoever might be outside. Colette remained at the big circular table that was the centre-

82

piece of the kitchen, her hands concealed beneath it. They grasped a Luger pistol, and it was trained on the door.

Etienne Barbut crossed the floor in a few rapid strides and opened the door wide. The next instant he was staggering backwards under the weight of the body that had collapsed against him. Barbut regained his balance and lowered the body to the floor, turning it as he did so. The pain-glazed eyes of Raoul stared up at him, then fastened on Douglas.

'You must get out, my friend,' he said weakly. 'The bastards are on to you.'

Colette hurried forward and placed a cushion under Raoul's head. As Douglas and Barbut knelt alongside, she deftly unfastened the French-Canadian's jacket and gently stripped away his blood-caked shirt. There was a gaping hole in his right shoulder; he had been shot from behind. The hole was plugged with mud which he had used in a desperate attempt to staunch the flow of blood.

'What happened?' Douglas asked, his face grim. He had a feeling that he already knew. Raoul took a sip of brandy from a glass proffered by Barbut and coughed slightly, but his voice grew a little stronger.

'It must have been only an hour or two after you left,' he said. 'When was it? Day before yesterday? Christ, I can't remember. Been on the run for ages.' He closed his eyes, and for a moment Douglas thought that he had fainted. But the eyes opened again, and Raoul went on: 'It seems the Germans found the tracks your aeroplane made when it landed. A patrol of them headed for the nearest village – you remember, the village where all the help came from when the plane got stuck. The patrol was under the command of a Gestapo official. The bastard didn't mess about. When the villagers wouldn't talk, he picked out ten men and had them shot on the spot. Then he threatened to start on the kids, at which point one of the womenfolk broke down and told him what she knew. Can't say I blame her all that much.'

He broke off and asked for a drink of water. Someone brought him a cup, which he drained greedily, holding it shakily to his lips with his left hand.

'That's better,' he gasped, handing the cup to Colette. 'Let me get up, will you? Shoulder hurts like hell, but I can sit up okay.'

'Stay where you are,' she ordered him firmly. 'You've lost a great deal of blood. Besides, I'm doing my best to dress your wound, and I can't do that if you keep on moving around.'

Raoul grinned weakly at her and allowed her to continue with her task of swabbing mud and dried blood from his shoulder. 'Okay,' he said. 'You're the boss.' His gaze switched back to Douglas, and he went on with his story. 'After the woman had spilled the beans, the Germans headed straight for my place. Luckily, somebody was out in the fields and saw them coming. I told the folks in my village to make themselves scarce into the countryside. I stayed for a while and kept Jerry's head down with some shooting, just to give the folks a bit of a head start, then I ran for it too – in the opposite direction. As I had suspected, the Jerries followed me instead of the villagers. One of them managed to wing me, but I found a hiding place and lay low. Fortunately, they didn't have any dogs with them, or I'd have been sniffed out for sure. As it was, the Jerries combed around for a while, then set fire to the village and went away. I knew I had to get a warning to you, so here I am.'

He made it all sound simple, but Douglas knew that getting here must have required an enormous feat of endurance on the French-Canadian's part. Wounded and on foot, he had crossed fifteen miles of open country, including two roads. The journey had been easy enough when Douglas and the others had made it on horseback, but for Raoul it must have been a nightmare – particularly in the knowledge that the roads he had to cross would by now be heavily patrolled.

Colette finished dressing his wound, raising him so that she could wind the bandages round his injured shoulder. 'You're lucky,' she told him. 'The bullet went straight through. You've lost a bit of tissue, but no bones were broken. I don't think there will be any permanent damage, apart from some stiffness after the wound heals.'

'Thanks,' Raoul said briefly. 'Now can I sit up?' Colette nodded, and Raoul was helped to a chair by Douglas and Brough. He subsided into it and winced as a stab of pain shot through his shoulder. He passed his left hand wearily across his eyes, prompting the remark from Douglas that he looked as though he could do with a good sleep.

'Sleep?' Raoul said in a tone that was almost accusing, staring at the SAS officer. 'There's no time for sleep. Don't you realize, the Germans will be calling up reinforcements right now, and that by this time tomorrow the whole area will be crawling with them? There was only one thing on your side right from the start, and that was the element of surprise. Now you've lost even that. You can bet your last dollar that the Germans are fully aware by now that it's British soldiers they're looking for, not just British agents – and it won't take them long to work out what your target is likely to be. You've got to move, and move fast.'

Douglas thought for a moment, then said: 'But they won't know where to look for us. Isn't it more likely that they will make an all-out drive against the Maquis in the hope that they will flush us out?'

Raoul nodded. 'That's what is worrying me. For the past forty-eight hours, the Maquisards who are to assist you in your mission have been quietly moving into the area west of Arles from locations all over Provence. On the eve of the operation they will assemble south of the road leading west from Salon-de-Provence. An SOE agent code-named Auguste is with them. Has Monsieur Barbut explained the arrangements London has made to contact you?'

Douglas nodded. 'Good,' Raoul continued. 'The signal will also be received by Auguste, who will then divide the Maquisards into two groups. One will attack and destroy lock gates on the canal that runs southwards to the Etang de Berre, drawing the attention of enemy forces north of Marseille; the other will follow the railway line south of Miramas and launch a diversionary attack on the northern perimeter of Istres airfield. You must be in position, at a place you yourself must select as favourable, and be ready to make your move as soon as the diversionary attack develops.'

'That's the immediate problem,' Douglas admitted. 'We've got to get into the immediate vicinity of Istres – which we have worked out might just be possible, by taking a roundabout route – but then we've got to stay in hiding until we get the signal to go in. That's going to be the difficult part. But I agree with you – what's going to happen if the Germans discover that the Maquisards are in the area too, and take steps to eliminate them?'

'If that happens,' Raoul said in a low voice, 'more will be jeopardized than your mission. We have two hundred Resistance men standing by for this operation – the cream of our men in Provence. If the Germans destroy them, they will also destroy the heart of the Resistance movement in this part of France. And the repercussions, the reprisals against ordinary French men and women, would be widespread.'

A sudden thought struck Douglas. He looked hard at Raoul and asked: 'You aren't thinking of calling off your men, are you?'

Raoul shook his head, and winced again as the pain of his shoulder struck him. 'No. I realize that a great deal is at stake. Sacrifices have to be made. I know that if the Maquisards were given the choice, not one of them would back down.'

Douglas relaxed, then said, 'But what will you do? You can't go back to the village, and you can't come with us.'

'Then I'll stay here,' Raoul told him, his voice faint now. 'I like it here. It's warm, and comfortable. . . .'

His voice trailed off and his chin lolled on his chest. Concerned, Colette bent over him. 'It's all right,' she said after a moment or two. 'He's fast asleep, which is the best thing that could happen to him.' She spoke rapidly to Etienne Barbut, then said to Douglas, 'He will be looked after. He will be taken to one of the *gardien*'s cottages, and hidden. He will be quite safe there.'

'Good. I wouldn't like anything to happen to him,' Douglas

commented. 'But we need to get ourselves organized. The sooner we move out, the better.'

Etienne Barbut had one of his servants cook a huge bowl of *bouillabaisse* before their departure. The SAS men viewed the mixture with some misgivings; the fishy assortment was almost entirely without taste, and the only item that imparted flavour was a helping of stale bread, toasted and strongly impregnated with garlic. Nevertheless, they finished their portions, feigning relish out of courtesy to their host, and being uncertain about the source of their next meal.

Afterwards, disguised once again as Camargue cowboys, they mounted the sturdy white horses and rode southwards, accompanied by two *gardiens* whose task it was to bring the animals back to their corral on the ranch.

It was still relatively early in the morning when the party set out. The sky was clear, a light pastel blue, and the breeze was sweet. For the first time since leaving England, Douglas felt relaxed and alert; a hot bath at Etienne Barbut's, where they had spent the night, had worked wonders for them all.

They made steady progress southwards, the horses following their sure-footed way along the eastern shore of the Étang de Vaccarès, its purple lagoons clouded with water-birds of every description. 'Just look at that,' Olds said to nobody in particular. 'I wouldn't have missed seeing that for the world. Just think – if it wasn't for old Hitler, I'd never have known the likes of that existed.'

The birds were their constant companions for several miles, until they turned aside from the Étang and struck out across country towards the estuary of the Grand Rhône. Far off to the south, Douglas could see what appeared to be a range of low hills, shining a peculiar white in the sun; Colette explained that they were literally mountains of salt, accumulated when the coast of the Camargue became flooded with sea-water during the summer months.

There was only one moment of alarm, when a lumbering three-engined Junkers 52 transport aircraft droned low overhead. The riders took temporary shelter in a dense thicket until the aircraft had passed; whatever its errand might be, Douglas thought, it obviously isn't searching for us. So far, so good.

After some hours, the riders reached an isolated thatched cottage. Etienne Barbut spoke rapidly to Colette, who signalled to Douglas and his men to dismount.

'This is as far as we go on horseback,' she explained. 'We lie low here until nightfall, then make our way down to the coast. It isn't far.'

Douglas swung down from the saddle and gave his horse an affectionate pat on the neck. He and the others bundled up their hats and ponchos and the two *gardiens* stuffed the clothing into saddlebags; then, without a word, they rounded up the horses and headed back towards the northern horizon.

The cottage was empty, but someone had clearly been expecting them. There was bread and cheese, and a pitcher of red wine, on a rough wooden table, and a fire of juniper wood crackled fragrantly in the hearth. Barbut offered no explanation, but indicated that the food was there to be eaten. They set to work on it willingly, their appetites sharpened by the long ride.

Something was puzzling Douglas, and he voiced his thoughts to Colette. 'How does he do it?' he asked. 'Barbut, I mean. I can't for the life of me understand how he can have told whoever lives here that we were on our way. It's uncanny.'

Colette laughed. 'Not really. Come outside, and I'll show you.'

She led him round the back of the cottage, and pointed to a small wooden lean-to hut. 'Unlatch the door,' she ordered, 'and take a look inside. But try not to disturb the occupants too much. They are pretty hard-worked, just at the moment.'

Douglas did as she said. In the gloom, something fluttered, momentarily startling him. Then, realizing what it was, he chuckled.

'Pigeons! So that's it. I suppose I should have guessed.'

Colette nodded. 'Yes, the Maquisards have quite an effective communications network in these parts. The only snag is that when the mistral is blowing at full strength, these little fellows sometimes won't fly. I can't say that I blame them; it's an evil wind.'

For some reason, her words sent a chill of foreboding through Douglas. Not for the first time since arriving in France, he felt a deep sense of unease. So far, everything had been too easy. He felt like a mouse, conscious that a nearby cat was about to spring, but not knowing when or where.

Darkness, when it came, fell swiftly over the Camargue. They waited for an hour longer, and then Barbut indicated that it was time to leave. Picking up their equipment, they set off in single file, with the Frenchman leading. Conolly moved a few steps behind him, obeying an earlier whispered instruction from Douglas. The Irishman's order was simple. If Barbut showed any sign of betrayal, he would die immediately.

They marched on, Barbut threading his way through great pans of salt that whitened the ground all around. Ahead of them, they could hear the murmur of the sea. Colette, who would have been leading the party over this tricky ground had it not been for Barbut's presence, moved up to walk alongside the rancher. The pace was slower now, as though Barbut and the woman were probing the darkness ahead in search of something as yet unseen.

Suddenly, a low-pitched whistle sounded in the night, off to one side. Barbut answered with a similar call and changed direction towards the sound. Colette fell back along the line of men and sought out Douglas.

'It's the man who lives in the cottage back there,' she explained. 'He has organized a boat to take us to the other side of the Rhône to the Golfe de Fos. There, we can mix with other fishing craft from Port-de-Bouc and Martigues. They come and go all the time, even though the Germans have tried to impose restrictions. With luck, we shall be able to go ashore unobserved at some quiet spot.'

The boat had been pulled ashore on the edge of a salt pan. They pushed it clear and waded after it through shallow water before scrambling aboard. It was a small craft, just big enough to hold them all. A man whom Douglas presumed must be its owner spoke in subdued tones to Barbut and Colette, then hoisted a small, triangular sail which immediately filled with the night breeze, propelling the craft away from the shore. The man from the cottage stood there for a few moments, a silent and unknown figure, then turned and disappeared into the darkness.

The boat's owner, at the tiller, touched a pair of oars with his foot and made signs that someone ought to make use of them. Douglas and Brough took one apiece and were soon helping the boat on its way. It followed the edge of the flat marshlands for some time and then entered the estuary of the Grand Rhône. The water was calm, little more than a placid trickle at the point where the great river met the sea.

As Colette had predicted, there were plenty of fishing craft about, some of them surprisingly displaying lights. Douglas thought that the Germans would have put a stop to that. Their own boat moved in anonymity among the rest, the man at the tiller holding a steady easterly course across the estuary until, at length, the far bank became visible, curving around a mile-long promontory into the Golfe de Fos.

The gulf itself was some four miles in width. With the SAS men taking turns at the oars, and the sail billowing nicely, the boat made good progress north-westwards toward the far shore and finally grounded among some marshy flats. The boat's occupants quickly jumped clear and helped to push the craft free before squelching their way towards drier ground. Behind them, a hoarse whisper came out of the darkness from the boatman:

'*Allez, vite! Et bonne chance!*'

Hefting their MP-40s, the SAS men fanned out in an extended line as the ground became harder under their feet. Barbut pounded along beside Douglas, breathing hard. Colette was a few paces to the rear. Reaching the dunes below some rising ground, well clear of the sea, they crouched down and took stock of their position. The night was ominously quiet.

Colette came up and knelt beside Douglas, who looked at

her questioningly. 'What now?' he whispered.

She pointed towards the high ground. 'See that rock up there? Just beyond it there's a little village called Fos-sur-Mer. It's about three miles south of Istres. We have a contact there who is sympathetic. He is the local priest. It was my original brief to take you to him, and I still mean to do that. Are you ready?'

Douglas got up from his crouching position and looked around before issuing his orders. Apart from his own men, there was no sign of life anywhere.

'All right,' he said. 'Let's go. But keep well spaced out, and freeze if there's any sign of trouble. We don't want a scrap on our hands.'

They set off up the slope, using a few small, dark bushy trees as cover and taking as much care as possible not to dislodge the stones that were strewn liberally over the area. The rise in the ground was not significant, and Douglas's team were soon at the top. Here, another strip of sandy ground lay between the top of the rise and a cluster of buildings a couple of hundred yards away.

Douglas and the others paused again, checking that all was well before moving on. Fleetingly, the SAS officer wished that it was light enough to get a better idea of the lie of the land.

And his wish was granted. For at that moment a searchlight beam flicked on, bathing the village and its environs in a piercing glare.

CHAPTER EIGHT

Instinctively, Douglas's party flattened themselves against the ground just below the top of the rise. The beam of the searchlight swept round from the village and traversed just above their heads, arcing in a swathe of light over the water behind them. It was a small searchlight, of the kind mounted on patrol boats.

A guttural voice called out something in French from beyond the searchlight. Douglas slid closer to Colette and put his mouth close to her ear.

'What's he saying?'

'He's ordering us to come out with our hands up,' she whispered back. 'It's clear that he thinks we are all French. They must have been watching the boat as it put us ashore. They must want to take us alive, or they could easily have shot us down by now.'

Douglas's mind raced. It suddenly struck him that the Germans, or the Milice, or whoever was up there, were not expecting to be confronted by a party of heavily-armed British commandos. They obviously thought that they had netted a group of the French Resistance. Whatever the truth, there was no way now that a fight could be avoided. Douglas wondered what the odds were, then dismissed the thought. It didn't matter very much, in their present predicament.

'Stall them,' he ordered Colette. 'Say anything you like – just buy me a minute or two.'

She squeezed his arm in acknowledgement as he crept over

towards the spot where Stan Brough lay. Conolly, he saw in the reflected glow of the searchlight, was close by.

'Stan, we've got to get round them,' Douglas said rapidly. 'They think we're a party of Frenchmen, probably unarmed. Take Olds, Barber, Mitchell and Cowley and work your way along to the left. The rest of you come with me. I'm going to create a diversion. As soon as you hear things starting to happen, go hell for leather for the village and don't stop until you're under cover.'

He turned and, followed by Conolly and the remainder of his team, crawled back past the spot where Colette and Barbut lay. The two were engaged in a brisk exchange of words with the men at the searchlight. Colette, playing on the enemy's uncertainty about whether the party was armed or not, was asking for guarantees that if they did come out into the open, they would not be harmed. Douglas noted with satisfaction that the enemy were taking no chances; no one had yet shown himself against the skyline, preferring to remain behind the searchlight in relative security.

After a fast crawl of fifty yards or so Douglas and his men found themselves just below a patch of scrub. Signalling the others to remain where they were, the SAS officer eased his way through the wiry tangle until he could peer through the last few twigs across the open ground. He saw at once that the searchlight was sited well to the right of the village, its beam playing in a short arc over the rise behind which Colette and Barbut lay. Words were still flying back and forth between the two sides, but judging by the increasingly high-pitched shouts from the vicinity of the searchlight the opposition was growing impatient. With the glare of the light in his eyes, Douglas could make out no further detail.

He slid back through the scrub to where Conolly and the others were waiting.

'Come up through the scrub to the edge of the rise,' he said quietly. 'Liam, I'm going to knock out that light. As soon as I open fire, send up a flare. When we've got some light on the scene, give 'em all you've got – grenades, the lot. It'll give Stan and the others a fighting chance of getting across that open strip to take 'em from the flank. Got it?'

'Got it, boss.' Conolly followed Douglas back into the scrub, reaching into a pocket of his overall for a small cylinder. It was a type of flare specially developed for the commando forces. Operated without the need for a bulky pistol, it needed only to be pointed in the right direction and then ignited by twisting and pulling a cap at its base.

Douglas waited until his men were in place, then slowly pushed the barrel of his MP-40 ahead of him through the last fringe of scrub. Snuggling down behind the weapon, he drew a careful bead on the searchlight. A tap on the leg from Conolly told him that the others were ready for action. Expelling a breath, he pressed the trigger of the machine-pistol.

The harsh chatter of the weapon sounded in his ears as he loosed off a full magazine at the searchlight. At the same time, there was a crack beside him as Conolly detonated the flare. Several things happened within a split second of one another; the searchlight went out with a tinkle of glass, the flare sputtered into life overhead, and three grenades hurled by Lambert, Sansom and Willings curved across the open ground. They exploded close by the searchlight, throwing out whining splinters and raising a cloud of dust.

Douglas slammed home another magazine, then rolled over again and snapped off a rapid burst at the figures he could see moving in the light of the flare. One of them dropped. To the right of the now defunct searchlight a machine-gun barked into life, causing the SAS men to duck as its bullets pounded a stream of dust and stone particles from the crest of the rise. Lambert hurled a second grenade but it fell short, its smoke momentarily obscuring the enemy weapon.

'Save your grenades!' Douglas ordered. 'Keep their heads down with your MP-40s. Liam, get another flare ready!'

The Irishman had already done so. Before the first flare fizzled out a second had taken its place, keeping the enemy position illuminated as it swung down on a handkerchief-sized parachute.

The enemy gun stopped firing for a few moments, and inexplicably a small group of the men near it chose that moment to change position in an attempt to get closer to Douglas's party. They ran into the concentrated fire of five MP-40s and were bowled over before they had gone twenty yards. The machine-gun resumed its vicious hammering, forcing the SAS men to duck for cover once more.

'I wonder how many of them there are?' Douglas said. Conolly ventured his opinion.

'Not more than twenty, I should say. Fewer than that, now. We've knocked out at least half a dozen. It's that bloody MG that's the problem. Could keep us pinned down for ages.'

Conolly sent up another flare, his third and last. Sansom said that he had two, but that was all. They had to do something to extricate themselves, and quickly. Suddenly, a voice yelled something from over on their left, near the village.

They looked. A figure came running from the shelter of one of the houses, zigzagging and firing in short bursts from the hip as it went. Douglas saw the helmeted heads of the machine-gun crew come into brief sight over their parapet of sandbags as they strove to shift the weapon round to meet this new threat.

'Cover him!' Douglas shouted. The bullets from his MP-40 spattered the enemy's sandbags. Beside him the others resumed firing too in a deafening cacophony that was echoed from the village, where more guns were blazing in support of the lone runner.

The machine-gun spat at him but he continued to come on, still firing. Then his MP-40 fell silent. He tossed the useless weapon to one side, then his arm curved back. Douglas clearly saw the grenade as it arced through the flare's dwindling light to explode with a flash and a crack directly above the machine-gun. There was a shrill scream and a man reeled over the sandbags, clutching at his face before tumbling to lie motionless.

The flare went out, but not before its light had revealed the lone runner sink to his knees, his hands outstretched to greet the earth.

'Flare, Sansom!' Douglas screamed, but the trooper was already igniting one. Its light revealed several figures, running away from behind the machine-gun towards the village. There were seven or eight of them, and they were chopped down mercilessly by the SAS men who had thrown themselves under cover among the small huddle of houses.

The echoes of the shooting died away. Douglas jumped from his position in the scrub, MP-40 levelled in case of more trouble, and ran towards the man who had been hit by the MG. He had fallen sideways and now lay curled up, his breath coming in short gasps. He groaned as Douglas knelt beside him and gently turned him over.

It was Cowley. The front of his overalls was soaked in blood, and Douglas knew at once that there was nothing that could be done for him. In the light of the dying flare his eyes flickered open and fastened on Douglas; they were already glazing over. The SAS officer bent low to catch the whisper that came from Cowley's lips.

'I . . . I did all right, sir, didn't I?'

Douglas touched the side of his face. 'You did fine, son. Just fine.'

A brief smile flickered across the dying man's face and his head sank into the dust. The breathing stopped. A bitter feeling of rage and helplessness welled up inside Douglas. He felt like pounding the earth with his fists.

Someone was standing alongside him. Dimly, through the blazing fury that pounded inside his head, he heard Stan Brough's voice.

'Bravest bloody thing I ever saw, sir. There wasn't a thing I could do to stop him.'

Douglas stood up, getting control of himself again. There was no time for emotion; soon, all hell was likely to break out in this corner of France. Brough, however, was right. Cowley's action was in every way deserving of a posthumous Victoria Cross; Douglas made up his mind that if he survived this

96

mission, he would put in a recommendation to that effect as soon as he got back to England.

He retrieved Cowley's identity disk and slipped it into a pocket. Colette and Barbut, shaken but unhurt, had emerged from their place below the rise and were standing off to one side, as though uncertain about what to do next. Douglas told them to go off and locate their Resistance contact, but to be back in five minutes.

Conolly came running up. He and the others had been checking the enemy dead.

'There are a dozen, not counting the machine-gun crew,' he reported. 'Fewer than we thought. Some may have got away, but it's doubtful. This has blown our plans somewhat, hasn't it?'

'You can say that again,' Douglas said grimly. The noise of the brief and bloody battle must have been heard for miles around. He looked down at Cowley's body. 'We've got to get him under cover,' he said. 'Liam, get a couple of men and take him down into the patch of scrub. Empty his pockets first. Bury him as best you can. The enemy may not yet know who we are, and even though they'll probably discover the body eventually, they may not do so for another few days. The longer we can keep them guessing, the better.'

A few minutes later Colette and Barbut came back, having made a hurried tour of the village. Its inhabitants were cowering indoors; they had been told that if they ventured outside, they would be shot. As far as the priest – their Resistance contact – was concerned, there was bad news.

'The Germans have taken him away,' Colette said breathlessly. 'Somebody betrayed him. But it seems that the Germans don't know the whole of the story. There's a rumour that they were tipped off about a landing here, all right, but apparently they were expecting a boatload of French commandos from Corsica. There have been several infiltrations along the coastline recently by small groups of saboteurs. I'm sorry, but I knew nothing of this. Someone, some senior officer with the Fighting French on Corsica must have decided to take the initiative and forgotten to inform SOE.'

'Well, he's got us into a hell of a mess,' Douglas snapped. 'The question is, where do we go from here? We've got to hole up somewhere while we sort this muddle out.'

Colette consulted briefly with Barbut, then turned back to the SAS officer. 'The only real cover within reach of here is about six miles to the east along the coast at a place called Carry-le-Rouet,' she told him. 'The hillsides are heavily wooded there, with deep inlets running into them from the coast. If we head towards Port-de-Bouc we can pick up the railway line and follow that for most of the way; it will keep us clear of the main road.'

She spoke again with Barbut, who shook his head and said something in a low voice. Then, surprisingly, Colette embraced him and kissed him on both cheeks. Turning back to Douglas, she said:

'He says that he will not come with us. He is an old man and slow, and will only hold us up. He will take shelter in the village tonight, and tomorrow will make his way to Arles to contact the Maquis. He says that you must not worry, and that he will contact you again within the next three days.' She hesitated, then said: 'Because of the change of plan, he has entrusted me with the code.'

Douglas did not like the revised arrangement, but had little choice in the matter. He reached out and shook Barbut's hand firmly and, in his halting French, wished the rancher good luck.

From the north, along the road that led past Istres towards Miramas, there came the sound of vehicles moving at high speed. It grew steadily louder. Douglas quickly got his men together and set off southwards at a steady trot, leaving Fos-sur-Mer behind. Fifteen minutes later, as yet unchallenged, they struck the expected railway line near Port-de-Bouc and followed it under an unguarded road bridge. They made a detour across country to avoid a small station and picked up the line once more where it entered the Chaine de l'Estaque hills, the name given to the elevated arm of limestone that cradled the southern edge of the Etang de Berre and ended, some miles further on, at Marseille. The countryside here was arid and devoid of settlement, for which Douglas was thankful. The hue and cry would be well and truly raised by now.

Presently, east of La Couronne, the narrow-gauge railway track curved into the beginning of a wooded area. Thankfully, Douglas and the others turned aside from the railway and headed down a slope, moving deeper into the shelter of the trees. After a few hundred yards Douglas called a halt and they sank down to rest. Douglas put out four sentries; the whole group, including Colette, would take turns at guarding the approaches to their temporary sanctuary. At first light, it was his intention to make a thorough reconnaissance of the area. That was the first rule: always establish a secure operating base and make sure that you knew the lie of the land round about. In that way, you seldom got taken by surprise.

Dawn came reluctantly through a partial overcast, finding the SAS party red-eyed and sleepless. Douglas, taking a final turn on sentry-duty, had ventured back up the slope as far as the railway line to see what lay beyond the wood, which now revealed itself as a mixture of pine and oak.

To his surprise, he saw that, a few hundred yards to the east of the point at which his party had entered the woods, a road coming down from the north-west crossed the railway by way of a stone bridge and then followed the line of the trees as it wound its way towards Marseille. He resolved to explore that section of the line, and the road, a little further at the first opportunity, and a few minutes later mentioned his intention to Colette. She told him that a few miles further on the road detoured in a northward curve to avoid the limestone hills, but that the railway ran through a couple of tunnels before it terminated in the port.

'Does it, now,' Douglas mused. 'Tell me – where is the biggest concentration of enemy troops in this area?'

She looked at him in some amazement, as though his question was naïve, then replied, 'But I thought you knew that already. In Marseille, of course. That's where the Milice have their principal headquarters, too.'

Douglas nodded. 'Exactly. So if we can block both the road and the railway line at one go – just before we move out to attack Istres, I mean – how much extra time will that give us before the enemy garrison in Marseille can get on our tail?'

Colette thought for a moment, her brow furrowed. 'Well, they would have to go in a big circle round the eastern side of the Etang, then approach Istres from the north via Salon-de-Provence. Let's see – that would be forty or fifty miles, at a guess.'

'Twice as far as if they were to come this way,' Douglas mused. A plan was beginning to form in his mind – a daring plan, but one that might just work, if luck was on his side.

'I need to know a number of things,' he told her. 'For instance, how often the trains run up the line from Marseille, and whether any of them go direct to Istres with supplies and so on. I noticed from the sketch-maps that there's a short spur line running from the main track to the airfield. It could be a way in for us. I think we've got to form our own concrete plan of action, and do it now, rather than depend on the Resistance for help. For all we know, the Germans could be mopping them up right now.'

Colette nodded soberly. 'You're right. I'm going to have to make a trip to the station in Carry-le-Rouet to find out what's what.'

'Can't have that,' Douglas said firmly. 'It would be much too dangerous. There must be some other way.'

'Well, can you suggest one?' she asked, looking him in the eye. 'Of course you can't, because there's no alternative. Look, I've got my civilian clothing in my bag, and my papers are all in order. They've passed inspection before, and there is no reason why they should fail now.'

'Why don't you let me go with her, boss?' It was Conolly who spoke. 'I speak passable French – enough to fool the average German, at any rate – and I reckon we could cope with most problems between us.' He grinned at Colette. 'I've a feeling you're not exactly a Lent lily, as the saying goes.'

Douglas stared at him. 'You've forgotten one thing,' he pointed out. 'Unlike Colette, you don't have any civilian clothing.'

'Well, I'll just have to liberate some,' Conolly said cheerfully. 'It shouldn't be too difficult.'

'Don't be bloody stupid,' Douglas snorted. 'You aren't going, and that's that. Colette has a chance of pulling it off, but you'd be just a liability to her.'

The woman smiled at Conolly. 'He's right, Liam,' she said. 'Let me do it my own way. I won't come to any harm, I promise you. However, if Captain Douglas agrees, I'd like you to escort me as far as the edge of the wood that overlooks the village. If I do run into trouble, you can cover my line of escape.'

Conolly looked questioningly at Douglas, who nodded grudgingly. 'Very well. But I can't afford to lose any more men, so take it easy.'

A few minutes later, Colette, having changed into slacks, a jumper and a pair of brogues, and with a headscarf tied under her chin, accompanied Conolly through the trees towards Carry-le-Rouet, a two-mile walk away, with a promise to Douglas that the pair of them would be back within a few hours. On the way, she found a small stream and paused to wash her face, removing the grime that had accumulated during the hectic hours of the previous night. Feeling more presentable, but still uncomfortably dirty, she and Conolly followed the line of the wood until suddenly it dropped away down the side of a steep inlet in which the sea lapped. A mile or so away, at the landward end of the inlet, lay a pretty fishing village with boats drawn up on the shore.

They followed the trees, which were becoming more sparse now, around the edge of the inlet – known as a *calanque,* so Colette informed her companion – until they were in a position to look down into the village itself. From their vantage point they could see some people moving near the boats, and a few more close to the houses themselves. They could also see the railway line, threading its way past the far side of the village.

Some distance to the east it disappeared into a tunnel, cut through a limestone hill.

'This is as far as you go,' Colette told her companion. 'Look – I can get down to the shore along that track. See it? It runs behind those rocky outcrops. No one will see me until I am in the village itself. Stay here and keep a good lookout – but if anything should happen to me, don't try anything heroic. Just get back to the others as fast as you can.'

'All right,' said Conolly, 'but be careful. We'd be a bit lost without you.'

She nodded at him reassuringly, then turned and picked her way down the slope until she reached the track. She alone knew the risks she was running; as soon as she entered Carry-le-Rouet she was bound to be singled out as a stranger, but she was banking on the character of the people in these parts to keep her out of trouble. They liked to mind their own business. Nevertheless, in case she should be challenged she had made up a cover story which was simple enough, and plausible; she was walking from Marseille to Arles in search of work. She had spent the night in the woods and now, finding that she had hurt her foot, she wished to know the times of the trains. She had a few francs for her fare. Also, to add to the degree of plausibility, she had wrapped a few pieces of bread and cheese – saved from the meal at the cottage in the Camargue the day before – in her headscarf.

She came to the shore and walked along it past the beached boats, stooping every now and then to pick up a shell or a shiny pebble – the sort of thing a young woman might do, if she were in no particular hurry. One or two of the fishermen who were busy with their nets glanced up at her as she strolled past, but showed no particular curiosity.

She reached the village and walked on down the main street. From a small café came a tantalizing aroma of fresh coffee and croissants. Her mouth watered. Dare she risk going inside? She had some Occupation currency on her, money now valid throughout France which was issued to every SOE agent. Why not? she asked herself. If she ate now, she could be more

102

sparing with her small share of rations later.

She stood outside for a moment, peering in through the window, acting the part of a young woman who was alone and feeling lost. Then she pushed her way through the door, starting a little as a bell clanged rustily.

The only occupants were two old men, who sat smoking and drinking coffee at a corner table. They took no notice of her. Uncertainly, clutching her headscarf, her bundle of bread and cheese in front of her, she took a few steps into the room and looked around. The old men continued their low drone of conversation. She coughed twice, the second time more loudly than the first.

On the second cough, a formidable-looking woman emerged from a room behind the counter, wiping her hands on her apron. The severity of her appearance was heightened by the fashion in which she wore her iron-grey hair, pulled tightly back and fastened in a bun. She looked at Colette through narrowed eyes.

'Yes, mademoiselle?' she queried brusquely.

'Please, madame,' said Colette in a timid and quavering voice, as befitted her appearance, 'I should like a bowl of coffee, with a little milk if you please.'

The woman stared at her distrustfully. 'You have the money with which to pay?' she asked. Colette nodded eagerly. 'Yes, madame. See.' She fished in a pocket of her dress and pulled out a handful of small change, which she held out. The woman stared at it for a moment, then poked it with a finger, as though expecting it to disintegrate. Then, without a word, she disappeared into the inner room, returning a few moments later with a steaming bowl. Placing it on the counter, she extracted some money from Colette's outstretched palm. Colette knew full well that it was too much, but said nothing.

'You also wish for a croissant?' the woman asked, her features softening slightly. Again, Colette nodded, and took the one offered to her. Like the coffee, it was piping hot.

'I regret that there is no butter,' said the woman. For the first time, Colette smiled. She said that it did not matter.

She took the food and drink to a table and sat down, looking out of the window as she ate. From here she could see the railway station, such as it was: little more than a short platform with a ticket office attached, perched on top of the slope above the village. It was only a short walk away. With luck, Conolly would not have to wait long for her return.

Finishing her coffee, she eyed the counter. There were some sticks of bread on it, together with a round of cheese and what appeared to be dried figs. She decided to buy some, to take back to Douglas and the others. It would be a welcome supplement to their meagre rations.

Going back to the counter, she placed her empty bowl on it and called hesitantly for the woman. The latter came out, again wiping her hands on her apron, and asked what she wanted.

'Please, madame, is it permitted to buy some bread and cheese?'

The woman looked at her with even greater suspicion. 'You have a ration card?' she asked.

This was the real test, Colette knew. 'Certainly, madame. One moment.' Turning aside from the counter, she reached down the neck of her jumper, bringing a snicker from one of the old men, and drew out a card, which though tattered and stained with use, was in fact less than a fortnight old, carefully forged amid the secret labyrinths of SOE in London.

The woman took the card from her and scrutinized it carefully, turning it over in her hands several times. At length, she placed it in a pocket of her apron and said, 'That will be quite in order, mademoiselle. Please come through to the kitchen. I have fresh bread there.'

Colette breathed an inaudible sigh of relief and followed the woman behind the counter into the room beyond. When they were both inside, the woman closed the door and said in a loud voice: 'There is the bread, mademoiselle. Please choose what you wish to buy.' Then in a quieter tone meant only for Colette's ears she added, 'This card is a forgery, mademoiselle.'

An icy chill clutched at Colette's stomach, yet her brain,

104

thanks to her special training, remained completely calm. Already, she was calculating how long it would take to draw the commando knife, concealed behind her other garter, and use it to cut the woman's throat.

She deliberately put fright into her voice. 'Madame – what do you mean? I do not understand.'

For the first time, the woman smiled. 'My child, your ration card is a forgery. I know, for I have seen others like it. But do not worry; it is God's will that you came here. You see, this village has no *mairie,* where new ration cards are usually issued, and so the authorities entrust me with the job. Wait one moment.'

She flourished Colette's useless card, then went over to a metal box that stood on a table by the kitchen window. Taking a key from her apron pocket, she opened the box and extracted a new card, upon which she wrote Colette's fictitious details. Then she rubber-stamped it and handed it back, smiling.

'There! Now you are once again legal, mademoiselle. Tell me – you are with the English, are you not?'

Colette gaped at her. 'Excuse me, madame? Again, I regret that I do not understand.'

'Pah!' The woman snorted and waved her arms. 'It is well known that a party of English commandos has landed in these parts – well known to all but the Boches and the Milice, that is. You come here, a stranger with a forged ration card, and therefore I deduce that you are not what you appear to be. But you do not trust me, and that I understand, on such a short acquaintance. Come a little closer.'

Colette leaned forward, still keeping her hand close to her dagger. The woman whispered certain words into her ear – words known only to key Resistance members in southern France, and to the agents sent to support them. She relaxed, and was immediately conscious of sweat trickling down her back.

'You are right, madame. I am with the English. And we need all the help we can get.'

Briefly, she outlined what had happened on the previous

night, telling the woman that the commandos had come ashore to help the Maquis in acts of sabotage – but omitting to mention the real target. That would be stretching confidence too far.

She told the woman that she had come to Carry-le-Rouet in search of food, then added: 'I should like to take a look around the place, particularly at the point where the railway enters the tunnel. It may be the line can be blocked there.'

'Maybe so.' The woman looked a little doubtful. 'Will you return later?'

'Here, you mean? Yes. I should like to take as much food as I can carry. And' – she smiled, a little wickedly – 'I have the money to pay for it!'

The woman laughed. 'Well, you had better take the bread you have just bought with you now, or it will seem a little strange to those old fools out there.'

Colette left the little café with her heart considerably lightened. It was as though she had just found sanctuary. Clutching her sticks of bread, she made her way up the slope towards the rail halt. An elderly railwayman – who, she suspected, also carried out every other function around the place – was sweeping the wooden platform. She went up to him hesitantly.

'Good morning, monsieur,' she said politely. He looked at her and gave a non-committal grunt before returning to his task. 'Excuse me,' Colette persisted, 'can you tell me the times of the trains to Arles?'

He straightened his back with difficulty and fixed his watery gaze on her again. Leaning on his broom, he leaned forward as though to see her more clearly.

'Trains to Arles? Trains to Arles? Everyone knows the times of the trains to Arles.' His voice was petulant, as though he resented this sudden intrusion.

Colette flinched away from the old man's stale breath and said, 'But, monsieur, I am a stranger. I set off to walk from Marseille to Arles in search of work, but I grew tired and, besides, I hurt my foot. I have enough money for the fare from here, but I regret that I do not know the times of the trains.

Must I wait all day?'

The old man cackled. 'Mademoiselle, you may wait until hell freezes, but it is unlikely that you will catch a train from here to anywhere. The Boches have suspended the rail service until further notice. It is to do with their confounded troop movements.' He turned and spat, aiming the gobbet carefully over the edge of the platform.

Colette's mind became icily alert. For a moment, her peasant girl disguise almost slipped, but she regained control of herself and said timidly, 'But, monsieur, I do not understand. Why should they do this?' She managed to squeeze out a despairing tear. The railwayman's gaze followed its course as it trickled down her cheek, and his heart softened. He reached out and patted her on the shoulder.

'Why, *ma chère*? Who knows why those swine do things. I know only that I was summoned from my bed early this morning by the telephone, to be told by my superior in Marseille – that fat pig Martineau – that there would be no more trains except German ones, full of troops, which would be moving north from eight o'clock tonight. That is the time the first one will leave Marseille. So' – he tapped his finger craftily against the side of his nose – 'so, I telephoned my old friend Bertrand at Miramas, who had also telephoned his friend Henri in Arles, to find out what he knew. Yes, he told me, the troop trains will go only as far as Arles, and then return.'

'Will there be many?' Colette asked. 'I mean, will it be long before our own trains will be running once more?'

The old man shrugged and turned his palms outwards, forgetting that he had been holding his broom. It fell to the platform with a clatter. He bent down creakily to retrieve it. 'Who can say, mademoiselle?' he said. 'I have told you all I know. You are welcome to use my ticket office in which to wait, if you so desire, but I fear it may be a long wait.'

Colette adopted a crestfallen expression. 'Thank you, monsieur, for your kindness, but I think I must begin walking once again. These are terrible times. Good day.'

'Terrible times indeed, mademoiselle. Good day to you.

107

And a safe journey.'

She turned and made her way back down the slope towards the café, her mind racing. In London, she had been thoroughly briefed on the disposition of the German forces in the Marseille area. The garrison there consisted of 7,000 officers and men of the 244th Infantry Division, commanded by a General Schaeffer. Now it appeared that a sizeable portion of that force was being moved up to Arles, and to Colette there could be only one possible explanation. The Germans were about to launch an all-out offensive against the force of Maquisards assembling in the area. They were using a sledgehammer to crack a nut, but that was their way. They would use hundreds, even thousands, of troops in a bid to encircle the Resistance fighters, throwing a cordon around the whole area and then systematically sweeping inwards, tightening the net. It was the type of operation at which the Germans excelled.

Somehow, the Resistance had to be warned. Colette hurried back to the café, quickening her steps. The grey-haired woman looked up from the counter in surprise as she came in. Colette noticed that the two old men were still there, but as yet there were no other customers.

'Back already, mademoiselle? Have you seen all the sights?'

'Yes, madame. I wonder ... have you some water with which I may wash my face and hands?' She inclined her head towards the kitchen door, and the woman understood at once.

'Most certainly, mademoiselle. Please come through.'

In the kitchen, Colette told the woman what she had learned. She hesitated, then asked, 'Madame, have you heard of a man named Auguste?'

The woman nodded slowly. 'I have heard of such a one. He is an Englishman, they say. I have heard those of the Maquis speak highly of him.'

Colette nodded. 'Madame, Auguste is in great danger. So are many of our Maquisards. I believe that those Germans are going to try and eliminate them. If that happens, it will not only be a tragic day for the Resistance in this part of France; it will also gravely compromise certain plans which are afoot –

plans that could affect the course of the war. Madame, I beg of you, is there a way that we can warn our men in Arles, to avert a disaster?'

The woman thought for a moment, then said, 'There may be a way. Wait here, mademoiselle.' She took off her apron and went out through a small back door. Colette waited anxiously for her return; she felt apprehensive and a little ill with anxiety. She prayed that she could trust the woman, although she spent each one of the fifteen minutes or so that she waited in an agony of suspense, half expecting the Milice to burst in at any second.

Instead the woman came back, bringing with her a tall, gangling youth with a spotty face and shrewd eyes. 'This is Louis,' she informed Colette. 'He has a bicycle, and runs errands all around this area. Everyone knows him, and he is completely trustworthy. On many occasions he has acted as a courier for the Maquis, and knows where people may be contacted.'

Colette looked at the youth earnestly. 'Louis, you are willing to help?'

'Certainly, mademoiselle.' The boy had a quiet and surprisingly cultured voice. 'Please tell me what it is you wish me to do.'

'I would like you to go to Arles,' she told him. 'You know some of our people there?'

The boy nodded. 'Yes, mademoiselle. I have delivered messages to them on several occasions.'

'Good. Then go to them and ask to see one Monsieur Etienne Barbut. It is certain that he will be there by the time you arrive. If something has happened to him, find the most senior among the Maquis and give him this message.' Briefly, she outlined what she knew about the enemy troop movements. Then she took a deep breath and closed her eyes for a moment. She was conscious that she was about to make the biggest decision of her life. She only hoped that Douglas would agree with it.

'Tell him also', she said, looking hard at Louis as though to

109

imprint every word into his memory, 'that the English will try and hold up the Germans. And that the main operation must be brought forward. It must happen tomorrow night. He will understand. Is everything clear to you?'

Louis nodded. 'Yes, mademoiselle.' He repeated it almost word for word. As he spoke, the woman who owned the cafe prepared a bundle of bread and cheese for him. 'Go now,' she said, thrusting the bundle into his hands. 'There is no time to be lost, and it is a long ride to Arles. May the good God go with you.'

The youth turned and left the café without a word, and Colette knew instinctively that he would do his utmost to fulfil his mission. She faced the grey-haired woman and took both her hands in her own.

'Madame,' she said softly, 'how can I ever repay you?'

The woman smiled. 'I am an old woman,' she answered, 'with not many years left, I think, before I go to join my dear husband. But before I die, I want to see my country free again. It was providence that brought you here. Now you must go, and do what it is you have to do. And some day, when this is over, come back to my little café, and drink my coffee and eat my croissants. And on that occasion, you will need no money.'

She pressed some more bread on Colette, together with some cheese, and pushed her gently through the café, past the two muttering old men. Colette kissed her on the cheek, then turned and hurried away down the cobbled street, towards the shore and the place where Conolly was waiting.

CHAPTER NINE

'You were right to make the decision you did,' Douglas said to Colette. 'Absolutely right. We've got to bring the operation forward. There's no other way.'

He turned to the Rhodesian signaller, Trooper Mitchell. 'Mitch, try and raise London on your radio. Send the code "Forensic minus 72." Forensic', he explained to Collette, 'is the code we agreed on for a substantial change of plan. What I'm telling London is that I am bringing the operation forward by seventy-two hours. There's absolutely no alternative. Tonight we do everything in our power to disrupt the German troop movements, and tomorrow night we hit the airfield. God knows how we're going to do it; we'll just have to find a way. Sansom and Willings, come over here a minute.'

The two troopers looked at him expectantly; 'Colette says that there's a tunnel just to the east of Carry-le-Rouet,' he told them. 'Do you think you can blow it, preferably with a train inside?'

'We'll have a damned good try, sir,' Willings told him. 'But we'd need to have a good look at it first, to find out exactly what we need.'

Douglas nodded. 'Right. We'll move out right away. We'll probably need to blow the road bridge near Fos-sur-Mer, too, later on.' He called to the sergeant-major. 'Stan, get everyone together. We'll move east, keeping to the woods.'

Douglas was sure, by now, that if the enemy was searching for them after the shoot-out of the previous night, he was looking in the wrong place. If the Germans still believed that they were dealing with a party of French saboteurs from Corsica, they must also have assumed that the raiders had gone north, to join up with the Maquis near Arles. So much the better.

Colette changed back into her overalls, keeping behind a tree for modesty's sake as she did so. The rest of Douglas's party checked their weapons and packs, ate a little bread and cheese out of the store she had brought with her from the village, and washed it down with clear water from a small stream that trickled down between the trees. Then they set out, moving in single file with Douglas in the lead.

It was hard going. Moving horizontally across the wooded hillsides, they often had to negotiate deep gullies, the landward ends of the steep inlets that cut into the coast. But it was a route that kept them well under cover, and the nature of the terrain was such that an enemy was unlikely to take them by surprise; a large body of troops would have been heard a long way off.

They passed a few hundred yards to the north of Carry-le-Rouet and eventually picked up the railway line at a spot where it curved back towards the coast on the last few miles of its run into Marseille. They followed the track down a fairly steep gradient and at length, when the trees began to give way to flat, sandy ground, they came within sight of the tunnel Colette had spotted earlier from the village. Here they paused for a while to spy out the lie of the land, and Mitchell took the opportunity to try and raise London again, but without success. Douglas told him to keep at it; it was to be the signaller's sole task until he produced a result.

They waited for half an hour. Nothing but seabirds moved on the lonely strip of land that fronted the sea below the limestone hills. At last, Douglas stood up.

'Stan, you stay here with the others,' he ordered Brough. 'I'm going down to see where the tunnel leads. You two, come with me,' he said to the two demolition experts.

Sansom and Willings shouldered their kit and followed

112

Douglas at a steady lope downhill towards the tunnel mouth, their MP-40s held ready against their chests in case of trouble. They sprinted over the last few yards of open ground and dashed into the shadows, Douglas turning briefly to give a thumbs-up to Brough, who was watching their progress from the edge of the wood.

Cautiously, followed by the other two, Douglas made his way along the single track into the tunnel's darkness, finding his way with the aid of the narrow beam from his hand-pump torch. He sensed that the tunnel was curving gently, and was right; as they moved further along a spot of light came into view, some distance ahead.

'How far d'you reckon?' Douglas asked his companions. 'I'd say about half a mile.'

'About that,' Sansom agreed. He was prodding at the walls of the tunnel as they went along. 'Surprised this lot hasn't come down already,' he commented. 'It's in a pretty lousy state of repair. Soft as putty in places. We'll see if we can engineer a bloody great fall of rock.' He grinned in the light of Douglas's torch.

They plodded on towards the far end of the tunnel, taking care to keep close to the walls so that their figures would not be silhouetted against the light of the tunnel entrance. Sansom and Willings conferred frequently with one another, selecting likely spots to plant their charges.

'Trouble with limestone,' Sansom said, 'is that it's powdery. You've got to pick just the right spots, or all you end up with is a few tons of dust. It tends to smother the force of the explosion. Still, we'll see what we can do,' he concluded matter-of-factly. Douglas had no doubt that Sansom knew exactly what he was talking about; he had been a highly experienced quarryman before the war.

They reached the far end, having completed their inspection, and Douglas watched in some fascination as Sansom and Willings began their task of turning the tunnel into a death-trap. What they were doing seemed simple, when they explained.

'What we do first of all,' Willings said, 'is to plant charges at intervals along the tunnel, at spots on the wall we have already picked. We place the charges in holes we drill as we go along – not a hard job even for a hand-drill, in rock like this, and they don't need to be big charges.'

He worked as he spoke, placing the first set of charges in record time. When he had finished, he carefully strung a length of very thin wire across the track at about chest height. It was attached to each detonator. The process was repeated at fifty-yard intervals throughout the length of the tunnel. Sansom brought up the rear, making some sort of adjustment to each detonator.

'Simplest thing in the world, sir, really,' he told Douglas. 'You see, going on experience, we've worked out the speed the train is likely to be doing when it reaches the tunnel. If it's the average length, it will take it about twenty seconds for it to get completely inside the tunnel and another ten seconds before the front end comes through the far side. So, here's what happens. Locomotive comes along and breaks the wire. There is then a timed delay of twenty-two seconds before the two charges back there go off. The time lag is progressively reduced as we progress along the tunnel, so that when the engine breaks the last strand of wire the whole lot goes off more or less at the same moment – near enough to make no difference, anyway. Get it?'

'Yes,' Douglas said dubiously, 'I think so. It all seems a bit problematical, though, doesn't it?'

Sanson looked at him in surprise. 'Why no sir, not really. We've taken all sorts of things into account – the approach to the tunnel, the maximum speed on this bit of track and so on. We'll be accurate enough, don't worry. That train won't be going anywhere after we've done with it.'

Douglas couldn't help smiling at the man's confidence. However, he had a question.

'Wouldn't it have been easier, to place your explosives under the tracks and simply derail the thing?'

The two men looked at him with expressions akin to pity.

'Good heavens, no, sir,' Willings said. 'People can get out of a derailed train, especially one that's been going fairly slowly, and start fighting. They can't do that if the whole caboodle's pinned down under tons of rock – even soft rock like this. They'll have to dig it out. Probably take weeks,' he added hopefully.

'Well, just an extra day would do,' Douglas said. 'Well done, both of you. I just hope it works, that's all, or we're in even worse trouble than we are already.' Privately, he was quite sure that the scheme would work, and that the task of extricating their men trapped inside the tunnel would keep the Germans occupied for a while.

They went back up the slope to the wood where the others were in position. There was nothing to do now but settle down and wait for nightfall.

While Douglas and his party maintained their uneasy vigil that afternoon, Louis, the youth from Carry-le-Rouet, finally reached Arles after a gruelling forty-mile cycle ride. He had stuck to the back roads to avoid being challenged; nevertheless, he had been stopped at two road blocks manned by the Milice. Luckily, his comings and goings between Arles and the coast, ostensibly carrying produce, had made him a familiar figure in the area, and he had no trouble in getting through.

Arles itself was full of Germans and Milice, parading on every street corner. Their very presence seemed to desecrate the ancient town which, in Roman days, had been a major trade centre and key port on the lower Rhône, rivalling Marseille. The Romans had made it their capital of Provence and later of the 'three Gauls' – the territories of France, Spain and Britain. Its links with Britain were close; it was here that St Augustine had been consecrated the first Bishop of Canterbury. Now, in 1944, the Germans had turned it into a grey place, a place devoid of its traditional life and colour.

Louis carefully chained his cycle to a set of iron railings and went into a small hat shop not far from the old Roman baths – all that remained of the palace built by the Emperor

Constantine – that stood near the banks of the Rhône. A middle-aged man looked up in surprise from some ledgers as the youth entered.

'Louis! What brings you here? It is not the day of your usual visit.'

'I have urgent news, Monsieur Bizot,' Louis said. 'I saw that the blue flowers were hanging outside, so I knew that no one was watching and that it was safe to come here.'

The blue flowers hung in a basket above the shop doorway. If they had been red it would have meant that the shop, a meeting-place for Resistance workers, was under possible surveillance by the Germans or the Milice.

'Well, my boy, what is it that I can do for you?' Bizot asked. Louis leaned forward across the counter and lowered his voice to a conspiratorial tone.

'Monsieur Barbut,' he whispered. 'Has he been here?' The other nodded.

'Yes. He was here a very short while ago, but he is here no longer. He came on the autobus from Port-de-Bouc, stayed for a little while to refresh himself, and then borrowed a cycle, saying that he had friends to visit. You know what that means. He seemed very agitated.'

Louis's heart sank. The expression "friends to visit" meant that Barbut had gone to make rendezvous with the Maquis at their nearby hideout of Les Baux. That in turn meant another cycle ride of seven or eight miles out of Arles, most of it uphill. But there was nothing for it; he would have to pursue the rancher as fast as he could go.

He thanked the shopkeeper courteously and went back to his cycle, looking round guardedly to see if anyone was watching him. There were two policemen on a corner opposite, but they were engaged in animated conversation and took no notice of him. He mounted his cycle and pedalled away slowly, so as not to arouse anyone's undue interest.

He took a small, winding road that climbed laboriously into the high ground north-east of Arles, past the low hill on which stood the former Benedictine abbey of Montmajour. Further

116

on, he passed without hindrance through the vill.
elle; and it was half a mile after that, as he approac
where a side-road branched off towards Tarascon, t.
into trouble.

Louis had dismounted from his bicycle to push it up .
but steep hill when suddenly he heard voices up ahead. Pus
the cycle off the road and hiding it behind some bushes,
crept forward under cover to find out what was happening
At the top of the hill, close to where the road forked, he
wormed his way forward until he was able to peer through
some scrub.

He saw at once that a road-block had been erected at the
point where the road divided. Behind it, that is to say on his
side, a German half-track straddled the road, the machine-
gun mounted on it pointing towards Les Baux. To one side of
the road a group of half a dozen German soldiers were sitting
on the grass, playing cards; a seventh was sitting in the rear
of the vehicle, behind the MG, smoking a pipe.

Something that looked like a tow-bar protruded from the
rear of the half-track. A man was trussed securely to it, his
head bowed dejectedly forward. A bicycle lay abandoned on
the road nearby.

Louis knew, instinctively, that the bound man was Etienne
Barbut. He also knew that he must do something to try and
rescue him from his predicament. But what? If only he could
get close enough. . . .

He retreated some distance down the hill and crossed the
road, working his way back up the other side among the
undergrowth. He made scarcely any sound, for this was the
way he often stalked rabbits and other small game in the
woods near Carry-le-Rouet. Reaching the top of the hill, he
lay still for a minute and surveyed every possible avenue of
escape. Fifty yards away to the left, a dip in the ground curved
round the side of a low hill; the hill itself, and those beyond it
that rose progressively towards Les Baux, were densely
covered in scrub. If he could release the prisoner and get him
as far as the first hill, there was every chance that they could

117

hide safely. It would take an army to find a couple of fugitives in that scrub, he told himself, and there were only seven Germans.

Cautiously, still under cover, he snaked his way forward. Reaching the edge of the road, he risked another peep through the vegetation. The card-playing Germans were out of sight on the other side of the half-track; he could still hear them talking and laughing amongst themselves. The German in the half-track, whose head and shoulders were visible, was looking the other way, puffing contentedly on his pipe and gazing towards the blue-misted hills of the Vaucluse that rose on the horizon.

Taking a deep breath, Louis felt in his pocket and pulled out a jack-knife, opening the razor-sharp blade with great care and gripping it between his teeth. Then he slithered forward into the road, inch by inch, until he lay in the shadow of the half-track, invisible now to the vehicle's sole occupant. The bound man had his back to him and Louis knew that he had to be especially careful, for a sudden move on his part might cause the prisoner to cry out in fright.

He crawled alongside Barbut, who sensed his presence and looked round sharply. At once, Louis raised a finger to his lips, cautioning silence. Barbut nodded in understanding. Working quickly, Louis sliced through the ropes that bound the rancher, who let out an involuntary gasp of pain as the circulation started to return. Man and youth both froze in apprehension, but there was no sign that anyone had heard the sound. The laughter from the far side of the half-track told them that the card game was still in progress.

Louis put his lips against Barbut's ear and whispered, so quietly that the rancher could barely hear the words: 'Follow me, monsieur. But be silent!'

The two crept away from the half-track. As they crawled into the scrub by the side of the road Louis glanced up fearfully, but the German behind the machine-gun was still gazing into the distance. Fighting against a desperate urge to get up and run, or even to move too quickly, the two crawled on their bellies away from the road, yard by yard, until they reached the dip in the ground Louis had spotted earlier. Just as they slipped into it, a hoarse cry split the air behind them.

'*Halt! Halt sofort, oder Ich schiesse!*'

'Run, monsieur!' Louis screamed in terror. 'Run like the wind!'

They scrambled to their feet and raced as fast as they were able along the gulley, swerving from side to side like hares. For an elderly man, Barbut had a surprising turn of speed. Suddenly, the machine-gun on the half-track opened up, sending clods of earth and grass flying into the air around the fleeing pair. The curve in the gulley, where it ran round the slope of the hill, was only yards away.

Then a searing pain lanced through the flesh of Louis's thigh. He screamed and stumbled but somehow kept going, driven on by the strength of fear. Blood streamed hotly down his leg as they put on a final spurt and rounded the hillside, plunging into the sheltering scrub. Behind them, they could hear guttural commands as the Germans launched themselves in pursuit.

Almost weeping with pain, Louis hobbled after Barbut. After a few more steps the two of them flung themselves down and began to claw their way up the hillside, keeping their heads well down. The scrub's rough branches tore at them, scratching their faces. After several agonizing minutes, they reached a particularly dense thicket and burrowed their way into its sanctuary.

The sounds of pursuit grew louder. Desperately striving to control their laboured breathing, Barbut and Louis crouched lower into the scrub, praying that the enemy would pass them by. Louis clutched his jack-knife, resolved with all the determination of his sixteen years that he would try and take at least one German with him if their hiding-place should be discovered.

Close by, jackboots crunched on dry twigs. The bushes quivered with the passage of a body through them. Louis cowered against the earth next to Barbut, certain that each of his heartbeats must be loud enough to be heard a hundred years away, hardly daring to look up.

There was a sudden exclamation, and Barbut seized the boy's arm. A shadow fell over them. Louis, forcing himself to look up at last, found himself staring into the muzzle of a machine-pistol. Behind it was a blond, bareheaded German, not much older than himself. There was a thin smile of satisfaction on his face.

'Hier sind die Schweine!' he yelled. *'Ich habe die Blutspur gefolgt!'*

Louis gripped his knife tightly and prepared to hurl himself at the German's throat. His eyes were on the knuckles of the finger that curved around the trigger. They were white.

There was a sudden bang and Louis hurled himself to one side, screaming. There had been no time to make his move. No time. It was all over. He dropped the knife and clutched himself, wondering where he had been hit.

But he had not been hit. Feeling alternately hot and cold with reaction, he rolled over on to his knees and looked wildly around him. The blond German was lying spreadeagled on his back, blood pouring from his throat. He was making feeble movements, his eyes rolled back in their sockets until the whites showed. Barbut had already seized his fallen machine-pistol.

A crackle of gunfire erupted on the hillside behind them. It was returned by the other Germans, who were steadily retreating down the slope. Louis looked round; some distance away, a man was waving his arm at them, beckoning.

'Allez!' he called. *'A nous, vite!'*

They scrambled up and pushed their way through the scrub, Louis limping and wincing with the pain of his injured thigh. Hands grabbed at them and pulled them down into cover. The firing resumed and now the Germans were in full flight, running for their lives down the slope. One of them threw up his arms with a scream and tumbled over and over like a shot rabbit.

The men in the scrub ceased firing and began to move back

up the hillside in relays, taking Louis and Barbut with them, each relay covering the other. There were a dozen of them, armed with an assortment of weapons. Barbut faced one of them, a stocky man with aristocratic features and a tonsure of dark, wavy hair.

'My friend,' he said grinning, 'to say that I am pleased to see you would be an understatement!'

'We spotted your predicament,' replied the other, 'and set out to give you some help. But it seemed that someone else had the same idea.' He smiled at Louis and shook him by the hand. 'Well done. You are very brave. But you are injured,' he observed, suddenly full of concern, looking at the youth's leg. 'Let me look at that.'

The wound turned out not to be serious; little more than a graze, but the bullet had taken a chunk of flesh with it and caused a lot of bleeding. It was quickly bandaged. Louis felt a flush of intense pride as both Barbut and the Resistance man showered praise on him; the pride became even deeper when he learned, later, that the man was the legendary Auguste, the Englishman who had come at great risk to help Louis's countrymen.

While his wound was being attended to, he told his story. When he had finished, the faces of both Barbut and Auguste were grim.

'This is grave news,' Auguste said. 'We thought that something was afoot when the Germans suddenly threw up road blocks all around this area. So they are waiting for reinforcements before launching an offensive against us, are they?'

'Yes, monsieur. But the English will try to stop them getting here.'

Auguste nodded. 'Good. And you say the English plan to attack the airfield tomorrow night?'

'That is so, monsieur.'

'In that case we must be ready to assist them,' Auguste said decisively. 'But first we must contact London to make arrangements. It was planned that a fast motor launch of the Royal Navy would land at a point west of the Rhône estuary to take the English commandos to safety once their mission had been carried out. Now we must change the timing, and hope that the Navy will have a craft to spare at such short notice. Louis, do you know at what hour the English commandos will make their attack on the enemy troop train tonight?'

'All I know, Monsieur, is that it will be sometime after eight o'clock,' the youth informed him.

'Very well. Then we must start moving down from the hills as soon as it is dark. It may be that the Germans will muster sufficient troops from elsewhere to attack us here; we must be gone before daybreak tomorrow. We will move into our positions closer to Istres and be ready to carry out our diversionary raids tomorrow night. But first, let us return to our headquarters; there are things we must see to.'

With two Resistance men supporting Louis, they made their way through the hills to the mainly deserted village of Les Baux. Even in broad daylight it was a ghostly place, perched on its spur in the hills. On a crag above the village a ruined castle stood; it had once been the home of a despot whose main amusement had been to kidnap local peasants and force them to leap to their deaths from the clifftop. Its advantage as a Resistance base was that the approaches to it could be held against an army.

After conferring for a few moments with Auguste, Etienne Barbut went into the deserted cottage which was used as an HQ building and wrote something on a scrap of paper. Emerging, he went round to a shed at the back of the building and selected a grey and white pigeon from among the dozen or so that roosted inside. He rolled up the scrap of paper and placed it carefully in a tiny canister, which he attached to the bird's leg. Then he raised the pigeon to his lips and kissed it fondly on the head before raising it high in his cupped hands.

'Fly straight and true, my little one,' he murmured. 'Fly to Raoul!'

He released the bird, which soared skywards in a whirr of

wings and circled once before setting its course towards the west, speeding low over the scrub-covered valleys towards the Camargue.

In the woods beyond Carry-le-Rouet, Douglas and his team waited for nightfall. Douglas was reassured by the fact that, after considerable delay and difficulty, Mitchell had at last established contact with London. His signal had produced a brief acknowledgement, and nothing more, but in the War Office the wheels would be turning to set the revised plan in motion.

From their vantage-point, Douglas could see across the bay to Marseille and, while the light lasted, studied it through his binoculars, making sketches of the strong points he could see and noting the types of vessel that lay in and around the port. Almost directly opposite, high on a cliff and surmounted by a lighthouse, was the Château d'If, the setting of one of his favourite boyhood stories.

Darkness brought the cold with it; not the crisp coldness of an English winter, but an insidious, numbing chill that crept into the bones. The mistral whined soulfully among the tree-tops, the only sound in the night.

'Do you think they'll be on time, sir?' It was Stan Brough who asked the question.

'They will be, if I know anything of the Germans,' Douglas answered. It was a few minutes before eight o'clock. They were all listening to catch the first sound of the train, but the continual moan of the wind made it hard to hear anything else.

Nevertheless, it was not long before his theory about Teutonic punctuality was borne out. After a few more minutes, they all heard the unmistakable chug of a locomotive approaching up the line. The sound was muted for a while as the train entered the first tunnel, then grew suddenly louder. A warning blast on the whistle signalled that it was about to enter the second tunnel.

'Any second now,' Sansom muttered, looking at the luminous dial of his wrist watch. Douglas found that he was holding his breath. The steady rumble of the train came to him as an echo through the tunnel mouth.

A succession of heavy thuds shook the ground, followed immediately by a muffled roaring. An immense blast of hot air burst from the tunnel, bearing with it clouds of powdered stone and smoke. The roaring continued for a few seconds, then ceased. A great slab of stone crumbled from the hillside above the tunnel mouth and rolled downhill, bringing an avalanche with it. Seconds later, it was as though the tunnel had never existed.

Douglas had been expecting a big bang, but nothing like this; 'Jesus!' he exclaimed. 'What did you put in there?'

'It's some new stuff,' Willings told him. 'First time it's been used for real. Quite effective, don't you think?'

'Quite,' Douglas agreed. 'Well, that train isn't going anywhere, and I don't think anyone is going to use that tunnel for quite a while. Let's get out of here before the fun starts.'

'What now, boss?' Conolly asked as he shouldered his kit.

'We're going back to Fos-sur-Mer,' Douglas told him. 'That's probably the last place anyone will think of looking for us. Besides, I want to be within easy striking distance of Istres for tomorrow night's show. I still haven't got a clue how we're going to get into the place,' he admitted. 'Somebody's going to have to take a good look at it.'

'I'll go,' Colette volunteered.

'No you won't,' Conolly told her firmly, and apologized immediately to Douglas for jumping the gun.

'Sorry, boss, but she's done enough. Besides, she won't really know what to look for. I speak passable French; all I need is a disguise. Let me do it.'

'We'll talk about it later,' Douglas said. 'First things first: let's establish a secure base where we can lie up tomorrow.'

As they began to move away through the trees, Douglas glanced back once at the ruined tunnel. He wondered if any of the troops on the train had survived. Over-gifted with imagination, he visualized the nightmarish horror that would now be gripping any who still lived, entombed in the reeking darkness. Suddenly, the night did not seem so cold.

CHAPTER TEN

Outside the windows of the War Office in London snow was swirling. It drifted down into the streets and formed a blackened carpet of slush in which people and vehicles squelched as they went about their business.

The depressing scene outside exactly matched the mood of Sir Richard Westerfield. He stood at the window of the conference room and stared out over Whitehall, marshalling his thoughts as he watched the eddying snowflakes. He rather wished that it were dark and the heavy blackout curtains drawn, to bring at least an illusion of cosiness to the room.

Brigadier Masters was sitting at the table, together with a number of other senior British officers, all of them members of the Directorate of Operations. The other officer was an American one-star general, who wore the shoulder flashes of the US Rangers. His deep suntan suggested that he was a new arrival in the wintry climate of England. He doodled on a note pad with his pencil, then looked up at Westerfield.

'What is the present position of the convoy, Admiral?' he asked.

Westerfield turned from the window to face him; 'It's west of Tangier, off Cape Spartel,' he said. 'The plan was to lie off Tangier for forty-eight hours to allow more escort vessels to make rendezvous with it, but now we can't afford that kind of delay. The orders have gone out for it to make all possible speed through the Strait of Gibraltar during the hours of darkness, and afterwards to hug the North African coastline before turning north off Sicily. We're just going to have to lose the extra two days in passage through the Mediterranean so that we don't interfere with the schedule for the landings. We can arrange some fighter cover from the airstrips in North Africa, but not much; most of our first-line fighter squadrons are in Italy, and will not be able to provide cover until the ships come within range.'

'So everything depends on this guy – what's his name? – and the French Resistance,' the American said flatly. Westerfield nodded.

'That's correct. But at least we know that Douglas is still in circulation. We can only hope that he and his men are still in a position to deal a heavy blow against the Luftwaffe unit at Istres. If they fail to do so, then the convoy must inevitably suffer severe casualties. We know to our cost what those rockets can do.'

'Well, I hope he pulls it off,' the American said grimly. 'Those are our guys in that convoy. I'd hate for them to have come all this way and be wiped out before they have a chance to fire a shot at the enemy.'

'Not only that, General,' Masters chipped in. 'If anything happens to the convoy, it will prove impossible to mount the landings at all. You know perfectly well what that would mean; this whole operation is designed to outflank the German Gustav Line, and in particular its central defensive position at Monte Cassino. If we fail to do that, the consequences could be disastrous – not only with regard to the progress of the war in Italy, but also in the context of future operations in western Europe. We need both men and equipment from the Italian front before we can mount an invasion of enemy-occupied France, General, and that invasion has got to take place this year. Quite apart from the pressure being exerted upon us by our Russian allies, there are strong Intelligence indications that the Germans are developing a whole new range of devastating weapons that could conceivably alter the course of the war in their favour.'

'I can well believe that,' the general said, 'if what you say

127

about these anti-ship missiles is true. But I don't understand –'

He was interrupted by a knock at the door. An aide came into the room and handed a typed sheet of paper to Westerfield, who scanned it and then smiled before addressing the assembled officers.

'Good news from Italy, gentlemen. As you know, the British Fifth Army opened an offensive against the Gustav Line four days ago, on the twelfth of January. The French Corps had an early success, making a ten-mile advance on the northern flank. I am now pleased to be able to tell you that the American Second Corps has occupied Monte Trocchio and advanced as far as the River Liri. Air reconnaissance indicates that the Germans are withdrawing several divisions from the seaward end of the Gustav Line in order to meet the threat.'

He moved away from the window and laid the sheet of paper on the table, placing his hands on either side of it and leaning forward slightly as he spoke.

'Gentlemen, the enemy appear to be taking the bait. They have left their seaward flank exposed at its most vulnerable point. This means that, with luck, our landings will be carried out virtually unopposed. If the reinforcement convoy gets through safely – and I have every confidence that it will – then in just a few days' time, the name Anzio will go down in history.'

Twelve hundred miles south-west of London, an elderly, rusting freighter churned its way through the Atlantic. The ship had sailed from Cork in neutral Ireland several days earlier and now, after one short stop at Lisbon to unload butter, had rounded Cape St Vincent and was on its way to Casablanca with a cargo of spare parts.

The vessel's elderly skipper leaned on the bridge rail, took his pipe out of his mouth and spoke to his mate, who now bore a livid scar on his brow.

'Bloody hell, lad, just look at yon lot. Like a flock o' sheep.'

Some miles distant, the sea was crammed with mer-

:hantmen – American-built Liberty ships for the most part –
with their rakish escorts scurrying in attendance like sheep-
logs.

The mate looked. 'Safety in numbers,' he commented. The
skipper looked sideways at him. 'Like hell! Look what happened to us, the last time we were in a convoy.'

'That's right enough,' the mate agreed. 'I still think they
might have given us a bit more leave after that lark.'

The skipper was unsympathetic. 'You had Christmas and
the New Year at home, didn't you? What more do you want?
If you thought that scratch on your head was going to earn
you a few months off, you must be bloody daft. You'd have
had to have a leg off, at least, with this outfit. Anyway, there's
a war on.'

'I'd noticed,' the mate said laconically. 'It looks as though
somebody's taking notice of us, too,' he added, pointing.

A destroyer had detached herself from the convoy and was
heading towards the freighter at full speed. She turned, the
water creaming white below her bow, and after a few minutes
of manoeuvring came up on a parallel course, within hailing
distance. The elderly skipper looked at her three smoke stacks
and her blue-grey splinter camouflage and snorted.

'Bloody Yank,' he said contemptuously. 'All starched uniforms and orange juice. You won't get a drink on one of those,
lad. Dry as a bone, they are.'

An amplified American voice rang tinnily across the narrow
stretch of water that separated the two ships.

'What ship is that?'

The old skipper leaned over the rail of the bridge and pointed
towards the bow, where his ship's name was painted.

'Can't you bloody well read?' he yelled. There was a pained
silence from the bridge of the American warship, then the
amplified voice said curtly, 'You are to hold your position
until further notice. Stop your engines and drop anchor
immediately, sir. This is an order.'

The tone in the American's voice brooked no argument.
The merchantman's skipper sighed and then gave the necessary

orders to the engine-room. The ship lost way and then the anchor went down, trailing a cloud of rust from its chain. There was no more word from the American destroyer, which increased speed and went away to rejoin the convoy.

'Wonder where they're off to?' the mate remarked.

'Couldn't say, lad. Could be Italy; could be the Far East through the Canal. I expect we'll read all about it in the papers. Well, we've nowt to do for a while but enjoy the view. See if you can organize some cocoa, will you?'

Unknown to the old skipper, someone else was also observing the convoy as it steamed past Tangier into the Strait of Gibraltar. Perched high on a rock near Tarifa, at the southernmost tip of Spain, a man watched the progress of the ships through powerful binoculars. He looked rather like a peacetime tourist, with his tweed jacket and plus fours – the kind of clothing a gentleman might wear on a stroll in the country.

In fact he was a gentleman: Rittmeister Freiherr Siegfried von Seydlitz was a son of one of Prussia's oldest aristocratic families, and possessed inherent sound taste and manners that had stood him in good stead during his career in the German diplomatic service. It was something the Spaniards appreciated, too, which was why he had many friends in high places – friends who saw to it that his movements around southern Spain, especially in the vicinity of Gibraltar, were never restricted or hindered in any way.

Now, from his vantage point, von Seydlitz was making an accurate tally of the ships as they came into view over the horizon. He counted the merchantmen and then the escorting warships, dividing the latter into the various classes – cruisers, destroyers and so on. With this completed, he set about making as accurate as possible a sketch of the formation in which the convoy was sailing. The Luftwaffe boys would need to know that so that they could plan their attack approach. Air reconnaissance would have been simpler, but it was out of the question; a lone recce aircraft venturing within spitting distance of Gibraltar these days could not expect to last long.

Von Seydlitz worked quickly, for he was conscious that there was not much time. The convoy was passing through the Strait of Gibraltar unexpectedly early – some three days early, in fact – and he knew that the Luftwaffe had only a limited time in which to attack it with their new weapons before it drew out of range or came under the Allied fighter umbrella, or both.

At last, he folded up his notes and put them in an inside pocket of his jacket. He pushed his binoculars back into their case, which he slung over his shoulder, and then strode off purposefully towards the cottage he had rented in a nearby village. He had spent the last two weeks there, watching and waiting, and now his patience had been rewarded.

At the cottage, he started up a petrol-driven generator which provided electricity for his radio transmitter. The necessary preliminaries took only a minute or two, for the transmitter was already set up on a table and its aerial erected on a patch of clear ground at the back of the building. The Spanish authorities knew exactly what von Seydlitz was up to, but they made no attempt to interfere with him. They may not have condoned his activities, but at least they left him alone, which probably amounted to the same thing.

Rapidly, under his expert touch, the Morse key chattered out the message that was to spell the death of the convoy.

So far, things had gone well for Liam Conolly. With the others, he had returned to Fos-sur-Mer in the early hours of the morning and, together with Douglas, had crept forward to make a reconnaissance of the small village. All traces of the previous night's battle had been removed, and so, it seemed, had the inhabitants, presumably rounded up and taken away for questioning. While the others took cover nearby, Douglas and Conolly searched each house in turn and came up with several articles of clothing which would make an effective disguise for the Irishman: a pair of baggy corduroy trousers, a tattered fisherman's jersey and a black beret that looked as if it had been used to shine boots. They also discovered a

131

rusting bicycle which Conolly pronounced serviceable enough for the job in hand.

Conolly stripped off his overalls, which he handed to Douglas, and put on the French garb. Douglas asked him if he was taking his gun with him, and the Irishman shook his head.

'No, that would be a complete giveaway if I should be stopped and searched. If that happens I'll just have to act dumb and pretend I've lost my papers. I'll say I'm a foreign worker, or something. There must be plenty of those about in Marseille.'

Douglas looked dubious. 'Well, don't get caught, that's all,' he cautioned. 'Colette says there's a small lake a few hundred yards east of here; there should be plenty of cover round about. It'll be light soon, so we'll hole up there and wait for you. Remember – don't stick your neck out. Just make a quick reconnaissance of the airfield perimeter, or as much of it as you can see, and pick out any likely weak spots.'

'I know the sort of thing,' Conolly told him. 'I'd best be off now. I want to get some way up the road before it's fully daylight. Wait a bit, though – a workman needs tools.' He flicked the beam of his hand torch briefly round the kitchen in which they were standing, and spotted a broom and a long-handled shovel in a corner.

'Those will do nicely,' he grinned. '*À votre service* – Liam Conolly, soldier of fortune and road sweeper *extraordinaire*.'

A few minutes later, Conolly was pushing his bicycle out of the village, his broom and shovel over his shoulder. The road on which he was travelling was little more than a track, but he knew from a study of his map that it joined the main road that ran along the western edge of the Etang de Berre a few miles up ahead, before the town of Istres itself. He had no intention of going into the town, for that would be taking too much of a risk; his present route followed the airfield's south-eastern perimeter for some distance, and he calculated that he might be able to see all he wanted from there.

He decided to keep on walking for a while. He was less

likely to run into unexpected trouble that way, for he could easily push his bicycle off the road and get under cover. In the gathering daylight he was able to make out much of his surroundings; the road ran through flat, sandy ground, with the great expanse of the Etang de Berre over on the right.

After a while he heard the clear note of an aero-engine, somewhere up ahead. He mounted the cycle, resting the broom and shovel across the handlebars, and pedalled on. Now he could make out the shape of hangars and other buildings in the distance, off to the left of the road. He spotted coils of barbed wire, running diagonally across the countryside, and knew that this must be the airfield perimeter.

He paused, and tried to locate the source of the aero-engine sound. It seemed to come from the far side of the field, and he guessed that the German aircraft were dispersed well away from the road and prying eyes. With this in mind, he could see little point in continuing in his present direction.

The other way, where the perimeter fence ran across open country, there was little cover except for some sparse bushes and wiry grass that rose knee-high in tufts from the rocky ground. He reasoned, however, that if he stayed close to the barbed wire and kept low, its tight coils would mask him to some extent from the eyes of anyone who happened to be looking this way through binoculars from across the airfield.

Hiding his cycle among some bushes, he crept close to the fence and set off alongside it at as fast a run as his bent-over posture would allow. The alarming thought suddenly occurred to him that the ground might be mined, but there was no time to worry about that now. He continued to run hard, pausing every hundred yards or so to watch and listen. The sound of engines still reached him, rising and falling, but there was no sign of any aircraft taxiing; it must, he thought be, routine testing.

After half a mile, still keeping close to the fence, he saw something rising above the grass in front of him; two long lines of posts, straddling the barbed wire and stretching away on either side. He knew at once that these were the approach lights, funnelling in towards the end of the airfield's north-south runway; there was another runway, running from east to west.

And he saw something else, something that made him crouch low in the grass. A few hundred yards away to his left, several grassy mounds flanked the approach lane. One of them, he could swear, had just moved.

He left the shelter of the fence and crawled towards the mounds on all fours, taking care to keep his head below the level of the grass. After a few minutes he fancied that he could hear voices, so he raised his head to take a cautious look.

The mound that had moved was a 37-mm quick-firing Flak gun, mounted on a half-track. Its crew were moving around it, making adjustments to the camouflage netting. A thin spiral of smoke rose from nearby; breakfast was being cooked. Conolly felt his mouth start to water, and fought down a sudden desperate craving for a hot meal. Up to this moment he had not fully realized how hungry he was – how tired, for that matter.

Conolly quickly saw that the other grassy mounds were tracked anti-aircraft guns, too, all of them cleverly camouflaged. There were six of them, three on either side of the approach lights, making a short flak line. He had no doubt that there were similar emplacements at intervals around the airfield, probably controlled by a central command post. The fact that the guns were mounted on tracked vehicles also meant that they could be rapidly deployed elsewhere on the perimeter to counter a ground assault.

He backed off through the grass and eased his way back to the perimeter fence, having first made a rough estimate of the number of troops at the Flak site. It looked like four per gun, with a few supporting personnel – say about thirty in all.

He still needed to see where the aircraft were. He continued his progress along the line of barbed wire, moving more slowly now because of the need to conceal himself from the gun crews. Eventually, with the guns well in the background, he was able to adopt his previous crouching run.

At last, peering through the barbed wire, he saw the first Dornier – or rather its nose, for the rest of it was hidden in a sandbagged and camouflaged revetment. A slight morning mist was now clearing rapidly, and through it he could see other, similar revetments. Tiny figures, presumably belonging to mechanics, were moving around them. Two or three vehicles that looked like fuel bowsers were in evidence near the hangars. Beyond the latter stood a line of smaller aircraft – the Focke-Wulf fighters brought in for air defence.

As far as Conolly could see, the bombers in their blast-proof revetments and the fighters beyond formed a rough semi-circle along the western side of the airfield, with the hangars and other airfield buildings in between them. To reach them from any angle would mean crossing a large expanse of bare ground, with no cover at all. Not even the most short-sighted of guards could fail to notice movement on it.

Thoughtfully, he doubled back along the fence, dropping down to a crawl once more as he approached the Flak emplacement. The germ of an idea was beginning to form in his mind, but there was no time now to develop it beyond that; his priority was to get back to Douglas and tell the officer what he had seen.

The half-run, half-crawl back along the perimeter fence seemed to take him twice as long as it had done on the outward journey. At last he came to the narrow road and made for the bushes where he had hidden his cycle.

It was not there. The broom and shovel were still there, but the bicycle was gone.

With infinite care, crouching down and looking around him, he rolled up his right trouser leg and unsheathed the commando knife that was strapped there. An instant later, he froze as a man stood up in full view from concealment on the far side of the clump of bushes. He too held a knife, a long stiletto blade.

Conolly recognized him at once. It was the Frenchman Jean-Pierre, the man with whom he had fought shortly after arriving in France.

Jean-Pierre adopted a half-crouching stance and sidled round the bushes. He was the first to speak.

'You have lost something, English pig? I have been waiting here for you and your friends. Now I am going to kill you and then locate the others.'

'I'm an Irish pig, actually,' Conolly said levelly. 'So, you have changed sides, have you?'

The Frenchman spat. 'I have no love for the English. Besides, when the Germans discovered the tracks of your aeroplane they said that they would pay well for information leading to your elimination. They were pleased to accept my services. They could not find you, but I told them that I would find you, and I was right. All night long I have waited here, knowing that you would come to the airfield. My task was only to keep watch on you and inform the Germans that you were here. But then I recognized you. I could have killed you at once, but I decided to wait a while and see what you were up to. Now I will kill you.'

'You are a repulsive pile of excrement,' Conolly said. 'Clearly, your mother was raped by a mangy billy-goat.'

Jean-Pierre gave a snarl of rage and lunged forward like a striking snake. It was exactly the reaction Conolly had hoped for. He side-stepped swiftly and then pirouetted on his toes, swinging his knife in a low and short arc. The tip of the blade ripped across Jean-Pierre's shirt front and the Frenchman yelled out in pain. He turned to face Conolly again. There was a red mark across his ragged shirt, but Conolly knew that the damage was not serious.

He continued to throw taunts and insults at the Frenchman, knowing that the man, of limited intelligence, would lose his temper more and more until, with luck, he made a fatal slip.

Hatred and rage blazed in Jean-Pierre's piggy eyes. He came at Conolly again, weaving and feinting. He lunged, and the blade of his knife snickered so close past Conolly's face as he dodged the move that he felt the breeze from it. Careful, Liam, he told himself; this bastard is good, better perhaps than you give him credit for.

136

The two of them fought in silence now, thrusting and parrying one another's blows, their breath coming in short gasps. Try as he might, Conolly could not penetrate the other's guard. Once he thought he saw an opening, but mistimed his thrust and got a painful slash across the forearm. Only his borrowed baggy jacket saved him from more serious hurt.

They fought on a circle of trampled grass, specked with drops of blood. It was damp with dew and slippery. All at once Jean-Pierre, throwing caution aside, hurled himself at Conolly in a frenzy, making slashing motions with his knife. Conolly, taken by surprise by this unexpected manoeuvre, side-stepped and curved his body to avoid the Frenchman's blade. The next instant his feet went from under him and he found himself on his back, sprawling partly among the bushes, his knife flying from his hand.

With a howl of triumph, Jean-Pierre brandished his knife and threw himself headlong at the prone SAS man. Conolly scrabbled frantically for his knife, and instead his fingers closed around a hard, round object. It was the haft of the shovel he had abandoned previously.

He thrust it forward and upward like a spear, using all his strength. By sheer good luck, the blade was pointing towards Jean-Pierre. It slammed into the Frenchman's stomach with a jar that tingled all the way up Conolly's arm and the man jack-knifed, plunging head first into the bushes beside the Irishman. Conolly rolled clear, still grasping the shovel, and swung himself upright, wielding the shovel above his head in the same movement.

Jean-Pierre clawed at the bushes and tried to get to his knees. Half-rising, he turned to face Conolly. The hand holding the slim stiletto came up and Conolly knew in a split second that the man intended to throw it. He never got the chance.

Conolly brought the shovel down with all the power he could muster. The blade struck Jean-Pierre edge on in the centre of the face and he fell back poleaxed, spurting blood. Conolly pulled back the dripping shovel and struck again for good measure, the blade taking Jean-Pierre in the throat. More blood spurted like a fountain, then subsided into a thick stream.

Gasping with the exertion, Conolly looked down at the twitching body. The double blow had split the Frenchman's skull and almost severed his head from his neck.

Feeling a little sick, he dragged the streaming corpse under cover of the bushes and added to its concealment with handfuls of grass. His own wound was not serious; although it was still bleeding the flow was stopping gradually as the blood congealed. He paused for a few seconds and looked around him, but as far as he could see no one seemed to have witnessed the struggle; the road to Istres remained deserted, and the German anti-aircraft crews were too far off to have seen anything.

He searched around, and presently discovered his bicycle where the Frenchman had thrown it, on the far side of the road. He did not intend to linger in these parts any longer. Mounting the rusty machine, he pedalled as fast as he could towards Fos-sur-Mer.

CHAPTER ELEVEN

The assembled Luftwaffe crews of Kampfgruppe 100 rose
to their feet and sprang stiffly to attention as General von
Falkenberg strode into the briefing room, closely followed by
their commanding officer, Colonel Karl Preuss, and a small
galaxy of staff officers. There was utter silence in the room,
except for the rhythmic tramp of the newcomer's boots as they
approached the raised dais at the far end of the room.

Von Falkenberg sat down in a chair to one side of the dais.
Preuss nodded to the staff officers, who also sat down, and then
faced the assembled crews, his feet planted at the regulation
distance apart, his hands clasped behind his back.

'Be seated, gentlemen,' he said. The crews obeyed with a
scraping of chairs and benches.

'We go tonight,' Preuss told them, somewhat dramatically.
There was a buzz of conversation that was quickly stilled as
he raised a hand for silence.

'The enemy convoy is approaching the Strait of Gibraltar
somewhat sooner than we anticipated,' he continued. 'Our
latest intelligence indicates that it is steaming at approximately
eight knots and that its leading echelons will be abeam Gibraltar shortly before first light.'

He surveyed the faces of his crews for a few moments before
going on. A few – pitifully few – had been with the Group for
as long as himself, almost from its beginning. Many were
newcomers, some already openly cynical like himself, but
others fired with enthusiasm to die for the Fatherland. Well,

139

he thought grimly, many might be granted that wish before the night was through.

'This operation', he told them, 'involves a maximum-range flight of some thirteen hundred nautical miles, there and back.' He used the term *Seemeilen* rather than kilometres, which most Luftwaffe units used out of habit. It was a throwback to his days as an airline captain.

'You all know the Dornier's maximum range with the kind of load we shall be carrying, so I don't need to remind you that there will be no room for navigational errors. Neither will there be any time for dummy runs in the target area; we will have to get everything right first time. So, to make absolutely certain, we shall close to within five miles before launching our missiles.'

There was another subdued buzz, this time with a note of apprehension behind it. Once again, Preuss held up his hand.

'We shall have one major factor in our favour. We shall attack at sunrise, just as the main body of the convoy is passing Gibraltar. As we shall be approaching from the east, the sun will be in the eyes of the enemy gunners. We, on the other hand, should be able to see our targets clearly. If the weather forecast holds good we should have a slight tailwind component to assist us on the outward flight. Nevertheless, we shall be airborne for approximately four and a half hours before the target is sighted, most of it in the dark. Everything depends on accurate timing; the last aircraft must be off the ground by 03.00. Now, before I go into more technical details, General von Falkenberg wishes to address you.'

Once again, the men in the room sprang to attention as von Falkenberg rose from his seat and came to stand on the edge of the dais. He did not invite them to sit down. Instead, he looked down his nose at them and delivered his monologue in what he considered to be clipped and precise tones, as befitted a senior Prussian officer.

'Men,' he cried, 'the Führer expects that every man will do his duty!'

Preuss, who was only half listening, raised a sardonic

eyebrow and almost allowed a smile to cross his face. He wondered whether von Falkenberg was a student of Napoleon's wars. After all, Cape Trafalgar was not so very far away from Gibraltar. Was it not the English admiral, Nelson, who had exhorted his men to do their duty before that battle? But perhaps the similarity between von Falkenberg's words and those of Nelson was merely coincidental. If not, the general had clearly forgotten that the English had emerged victorious from that encounter.

'You have the unique opportunity,' the general went on, 'to sweep the British and Americans from the seas! Never before have weapons such as these been placed in the hands of German warriors!'

From somewhere in the middle of the room there came a deep groan. Von Falkenberg glared, and so did one or two of the earnest newcomers to the Group, but the rest of the assembled crews maintained expressions of blank innocence. The general chose to ignore the interruption. He lowered his voice to what he believed to be a conspiratorial level. After all, one sometimes had to speak to these fellows man to man.

'Soon, perhaps very soon, the Allies will perpetuate their greatest folly of the war. They will attempt to land in France. Needless to say, they will be thrown back into the sea by the defences of our great Atlantic Wall. But we can turn their inevitable defeat into a massacre, a military disaster unparalleled in history.'

Preuss was wondering if von Falkenberg was aware of the events of a year ago, when the German Sixth Army had lost 100,000 men at Stalingrad. Fortunately, the general's talents did not extend to reading thoughts. He went on unperturbed, warming to his theme.

'The Führer has given his personal guarantee that, if you, the men of Kampfgruppe 100, succeed in destroying the Gibraltar convoy, he will order the priority production of anti-shipping missiles in their thousands.'

It's a pity he hasn't taken that step already, Preuss thought. After we use up our stockpile there won't be any more, unless

141

Hitler gets off his backside.

'So,' von Falkenberg continued, 'much depends on your performance tonight. If you succeed, Germany will owe you a great debt of gratitude. But if you should fail....'

He left the sentence unfinished and stalked back to his seat in triumph. Wearily, Preuss got up and took his place. For the second time, he told his men to sit down. That, he reflected, was exactly the kind of morale-boosting pep talk they could all do without.

Half an hour later, with the preliminary briefing over, the crews split up to carry out their individual duties before attempting to snatch a few hours' sleep. Preuss, in a rage, locked himself in his office and kicked a waste-paper basket across the room; von Falkenberg had just informed him that he would be flying with Preuss's crew 'to observe results'.

Outside, as the afternoon wore on, Istres became the scene of intense activity. The aircraft had already been checked over that morning, and their engines run-up, and now the ground crews worked flat out to ensure that every machine was fully serviceable for the night's operation. In the underground weapons store, armourers and specialist engineers checked and re-checked the complex systems of the Fritz-z missiles, which would be fuelled and mated with their parent aircraft later in the day.

The guards around the airfield perimeter were doubled and all gun crews placed on full alert. A few trustworthy French civilians, employed by the Germans as cleaners and handymen on the recommendation of the local Milice, were curtly told to leave the base as quickly as possible and go home.

One of them, who had quietly spent the last ten minutes listening to the conversation of two German pilots as he swept the corridor outside their quarters, cycled along a towpath that ran beside the bank of a small river north of Istres. The waterway flowed from its parent river, the Rhône, from Arles to the Étang de Berre.

After a few miles, the cyclist paused to pass the time of day with a man who sat fishing by the bridge that crossed the river

142

between Arles and Salon-de-Provence.

'Good day, monsieur,' he said. 'The fishing, is it good?'

The other shook his head. 'Not so good. How is it with you?'

The cyclist looked around carefully, then said: 'I have news, monsieur. The mission flies at three in the morning, perhaps a little earlier.'

The fisherman nodded. 'Thank you. You have made my wait worthwhile. Better go on your way now. But go carefully – the red flowers are hanging outside the hat shop in Arles.'

'Thank you. I shall take heed of your warning.' The man mounted his cycle and moved off up the road. The fisherman watched him go, then rapidly began to dismantle his tackle. Etienne Barbut had work to do.

Conolly, meanwhile, had encountered no further trouble on the way back to Fos-sur-Mer. Leaving his bicycle where he had found it, he had made his way down to the shore of the small lake and, after scouting around for some time, had eventually found Douglas – or rather had been found by Douglas, who had stayed in hiding until he was absolutely certain that it was the Irishman who was approaching. Conolly made his report to Douglas, who listened in silence and then quietly confessed that he was worried about their immediate future.

'You can see right across the lake from here,' he said, 'as far as the road that runs past this side of the Étang de Berre. Here, take a look through the binoculars.'

Conolly did so, and spotted three military trucks parked on the far side of the lake. 'See what I mean?' Douglas asked. 'They've been there for about an hour. They're French, I think, rather than German. We counted forty or fifty bodies getting out of them. They moved off in both directions along the lake. My bet is that the Germans are still preoccupied with digging their blokes out of the tunnel that we sabotaged and have called on the Milice for help. They know roughly the area we're in; I expect they've already searched the woods near

Carry-le-Rouet.'

'Do you think we ought to make a move, boss?' Conolly asked him. Douglas shook his head. 'No, we'll stay put. There's only one way to go from here, and that's towards Istres. We'll hide in the lake if we have to. Things will be easier after dark. At least we now know the layout of the target, thanks to you. I just wish we knew one or two things more — such as what time the Resistance people are going to launch their attack.'

Douglas passed a grimy hand over his eyes. He felt desperately tired, but dare not even lapse into a doze. That was a privilege he had accorded to the others, who were taking it in turn to snatch some sleep for a while, oblivious to the chilly and damp conditions among the reeds at the lakeside. Whoever had designed their overalls, he thought, had done a good job. It was quite possible to lie in an inch of water while wearing them and not get wet.

He handed over Conolly's overalls. The Irishman gratefully stripped off his smelly French clothing and put on the one-piece garment, checking the assorted weaponry that was tucked away in the various pockets. 'That's much better,' he grinned, reaching out for his MP-40, which Douglas had also kept safely for him. 'I feel properly dressed, now.'

There was a sudden movement among the reeds and Stan Brough appeared, looking concerned.

'I'm worried about Colette, sir,' he said. 'She's not well. Will you have a look at her?'

Douglas nodded and followed the sergeant-major through the sodden reeds to where Colette lay some distance away, her head pillowed on her haversack. Her teeth were chattering and sweat stood out on her forehead. Nevertheless, she managed a weak smile as Douglas crawled up, and raised herself on one elbow. He asked her what was the matter.

'Nothing, really,' she told him. 'I seem to have caught a nasty cold, that's all. My legs are a bit shaky. It's nothing that a good meal and a hot drink wouldn't cure.'

'Can you hang on?' Douglas asked her anxiously.

She smiled again. 'Of course I can,' she said. 'In any case,

144

if you think I can't keep up, you know what to do. You'll just have to leave me behind. Nothing, least of all a silly, sick woman, must be allowed to jeopardize the success of this mission.'

'Maybe some of this will help. I've been saving it for an emergency, and I guess this is one.'

It was Conolly who spoke. He had followed Douglas through the reeds and now, from an overall pocket, he took a hip flask. Unscrewing the cap, he poured a measure of liquid into it and handed it to Colette with the instruction to 'knock it straight back.' She did so and immediately gave a cough, her face reddening. It was neat cognac.

Conolly put the cap back on the hip flask and stowed it away again. 'There now,' he said, 'that'll keep the collywobbles away. And none of you blighters are getting any,' he added, looking darkly at Lambert, Barber and Olds, who were watching with more than just a passing interest. 'It's Colette's medicine, and that's that.'

The fiery liquor did much to restore Colette's spirits. 'I'll be all right,' she told Douglas. 'It's the waiting that's getting me down, that's all. As soon as the action starts, I'll be fine.'

'It might start sooner than you think, miss.' Brian Olds, who had been standing look-out, suddenly raised the alarm as his keen senses detected something. Quietly, Douglas asked him what it was.

'I'm not quite sure, sir,' Olds said in a whisper. He pointed. 'It's over there. I'm sure there's something moving among the reeds, and heading our way. Not a man, though – too fast for that.'

'A dog, would you say?'

'Might be, sir. But if it is, he hasn't much chance of scenting us, with all this water about. If he finds us it'll be pure luck. We're downwind of him, too.'

'Well, you never know,' Douglas said. 'Knives out! No shooting, mind, no matter what.'

They waited in tense silence, flattened against the wet earth, their ears straining to catch any alien sound. After a while they heard a faint rustling noise. It grew steadily louder, and they turned their eyes expectantly in its direction, their knives at the ready.

The rustling stopped. A few yards away, immediately in front of Olds, the reeds parted to reveal a savage-looking muzzle and then a sleek black head, with pointed ears turned down slightly at the tips. The animal's jaws parted, showing white, razor-sharp fangs. A deep growl rumbled in its throat and it slid forward another couple of feet until the whole of its body was in view. It was stocky and powerfully muscled, sleekly black on top and tan underneath.

'Doberman,' somebody whispered. 'Nasty bastards.'

The dog growled again. Olds, who was the nearest to it, made a sudden crooning, soothing sound, then began to talk softly to the animal. The others could not hear what he was saying. Douglas watched the Doberman's eyes, which were fixed unblinkingly on Olds. Every muscle in the SAS officer's body was tensed, turning his frame into a coiled spring that was instantly ready to go to Olds's defence if the dog unexpectedly attacked him.

Olds continued to talk to the dog in his low, soothing whisper. The tone of his voice had a mysterious trance-like quality about it, as though the trooper was invoking the ancient earth gods of his Anglian forefathers, the deities of oak and ash and thorn through which men, it was said in legend, could speak to dumb animals.

Still talking, he slowly reached out his hand towards the Doberman. The hound crouched low on its belly and sidled forward, inch by inch, its jaws closed now as it sniffed the air. Its muzzle snuffled around Olds's outstretched fingers and then, to the wonderment of the others, its tongue came out and licked them wetly.

Olds caressed its ears, crooning to it all the while. For two minutes he went on stroking it, then slowly withdrew his hand. The Doberman backed off and sat on its haunches, looking at Olds with its head on one side. Olds spoke to it again, more sharply this time, and it turned abruptly and bounded away into the reeds.

Douglas and the others let go their pent-up breaths in a collective whistle.

'Brian, you're a bloody marvel,' Conolly said. 'If I hadn't seen that with my own eyes, I would never have believed it.'

'Just a trick I picked up when I was a kid,' Olds said modestly. Douglas noted that there were beads of sweat on his forehead. 'Something an old gamekeeper taught me. It sort of hypotizes them, or something like that. Puts 'em into a trance, like.'

'Well, I hope it forgets where we are when it comes out of it,' said Barber. 'Wonder if it works with women,' he added thoughtfully.

'All right,' Douglas reminded them, 'we aren't out of the wood yet. The Milice are still around somewhere and they can't be far away, or the dog wouldn't have been sniffing around here. So let's keep quiet, and wide awake.'

They waited. Once, they thought they heard the sound of French voices, but a cautious peek above the reeds showed nothing. Towards the middle of the afternoon a high-winged spotter aircraft, a French type which Douglas could not identify, circled the little lake and then swooped low over the trucks that were still parked on the opposite side, as though dropping a message. Presently, through his binoculars, Douglas saw figures converging on the vehicles which, after a delay of a few more minutes, headed north on the road towards Istres.

Douglas wondered if the militiamen had been recalled to help reinforce the airfield's defences before nightfall. It was his bet that the field would be most heavily defended on its northern perimeter, where the Germans probably considered the main threat from the Maquis would lie. That was exactly the situation he wanted.

He felt dejected, hungry and miserable, although he knew that he must not show it to the others, who almost certainly felt the same way. Fretfully, he looked at the sky and prayed for the onset of darkness.

CHAPTER TWELVE

They crept through the wet, coarse grass, following the line of the airfield perimeter, stopping every now and then to watch and listen. The flarepath was lit and, on the far side of the field, aircraft were running up their engines. Beyond the barbed wire fence, vehicles moved around the perimeter track at regular intervals, with a minute between each one; it was obvious that the base was being patrolled in strength.

During one pause, Douglas rolled back the cuff of his overall and peered at the luminous dial of his watch. It was 02.30 and as more aero-engines added to the throbbing roar that echoed across the airfield, he realized that the German bombers must be getting ready to take off. There was no doubt in his mind now that the enemy had received word of the convoy's early passage into the Mediterranean, and were making ready to attack it. Time was critical, and there was less of it than he had anticipated.

Douglas made sure that Colette stayed close to him as they crawled on. She was keeping up valiantly, but he knew that she was under considerable strain and close to the point of exhaustion. For her, the next few minutes would be critical.

They paused again, and this time Conolly crept up to Douglas and tapped him on the arm, pointing ahead. After a few moments of searching the darkness, Douglas finally picked out the dark humps that were the 37-mm flak guns, mounted on their half tracks. The SAS men and Colette moved forward again with infinite caution until the guns were more clearly visible in the light cast by the airfield lights. Two helmeted heads were just visible behind the breech of the nearest gun, and Douglas guessed that the crews were closed up and ready for action. So much the better: it would make them easier to deal with.

Douglas put his lips close to Colette's ear.

'Stay here,' he whispered. 'You're in no fit state to have any part in this. When you hear me yell for you, come up as fast as you can. Okay?'

'Okay,' she whispered back. 'Sorry to be such a nuisance.'

He gave her a reassuring pat on the shoulder and, making sure that his MP-40 was slung firmly in place across his back, drew his long commando knife. Around him, the others were doing the same. The roar of the Dorniers' engines was very loud now, drowning out almost every other sound.

Douglas had already split his small force into groups of three, each group with the task of capturing a half-track and its all-important anti-aircraft gun. Stealth and surprise were the essence of the plan; the object was to seize the three nearest half-tracks and kill the crews without alerting the crews of the three guns on the opposite side of the approach lights. Three rounds of high-explosive 37-mm from the captured weapons should be enough to finish them off.

That was the first and all-important step. What followed afterwards would, Douglas was aware, be largely a matter of luck. With the German bombers getting ready to take off there could be no question of waiting until the French Resistance launched their diversionary attacks, even assuming that they were still capable of doing so. Douglas had no way of knowing whether the Germans had managed to send troop reinforcements to the Arles area by road, but he had already made up his mind to expect the worst. It looked as though the success or otherwise of the operation now depended entirely on himself, his remaining eight men, and of course Colette – although he no longer considered her to be in a fit state to take much part.

The three SAS groups now split up and crawled closer to

their objectives. Douglas was leading Olds and Lambert, Brough was accompanied by Barber and Sansom, and Conolly by Mitchell and Willings. As they crawled through the grass, Douglas snatched a glance across the airfield, through the barbed wire, and fancied he saw the navigation lights of an aircraft, moving round the perimeter track towards the take-off point. Time was fast running out.

Suddenly, Douglas and the two men with him froze as a figure detached itself from the nearest half-track. There was a pause, then a cough; Douglas realized that the man must be urinating against the vehicle's tracks, for he was close enough to hear the raindrop-like spatter above the noise of the aero-engines.

Almost without thinking, he bounded to his feet and was across the intervening space in a few quick strides. His left hand went up round the German soldier's face, closing like a vice over the man's nose and mouth. His head came back and the blade of Douglas's knife slid in beneath his chin, thrusting upwards into the lower part of the brain. The soldier jerked twice and went limp.

Douglas lowered the body quietly to the ground and crouched for a moment beside the half-track's armoured side, together with Olds and Lambert. From this position they could not be seen by the other members of the gun crew, who were at the rear of the vehicle behind the gun itself. The dead soldier had not made a sound, and no one seemed to have noticed anything untoward.

Still keeping low, the three SAS men crept along the side of the vehicle, close to the tracks. Then, after a pause to take a deep breath, all three launched themselves simultaneously on to the gun platform.

The fight was brief, one-sided and bloody. Douglas found himself face to face with a German who was leaning against the breech of the gun and struck upwards with all his might, aiming for the spot just below the pale blur of the man's features. The soldier gave a choking gasp and Douglas kicked him hard in the stomach, freeing the blade and at the same

150

time sending the man tumbling off the gun platform.

Douglas swung round to lend assistance to Olds and Lambert, but it was not necessary. Their respective Germans, taken completely by surprise, were quickly despatched and dumped unceremoniously over the side.

From a nearby half-track, the one being attacked by Brough's team, came a short, high cry of pain and terror, then silence.

Douglas turned to Olds and said: 'Brian, get into the cab, quickly. Start up when I give the word. Lambert, give me a hand on the gun. There's already a clip loaded; the ammo racks are there, beside you. Stand by to reload when needed.'

Douglas slid into the gunner's seat on the left-hand side of the breech and lowered the gun's long barrel, using a handle to traverse the platform until the gun was sighted on the half-track that stood directly opposite, on the other side of the approach lights. Someone must at last have realized that something was badly wrong; a voice, high and anxious, called through the darkness.

'Was ist los da druben? Hab' Ich einen Schrei gehört?'

'Nein! Es fehlt nichts. Alles in Ordnung!'

Douglas recognized the voice that gave the reply. It belonged to Conolly, a sure indication that there were now four fewer live Germans in half-track number three. If he had any lingering doubt, it was dispelled when, a few moments later, he saw the dark outlines of the guns on the two neighbouring half-tracks also swivel round to point at the vehicles opposite.

He worked the lever that slipped a shell into the gun's breech. Afterwards, the weapon would fire automatically as long as he held his finger on the trigger. He sighted carefully, aiming for the spot just below the gun platform on the other half-track, feeling for it mentally, for the other vehicle was nothing more than a dark shape.

He squeezed the trigger, loosing off a single round. The gun discharged its shell with a resounding crack and the barrel recoiled. A dull red spot appeared instantaneously on the side of the target. The next instant, the half-track exploded with a

151

crash and a sheet of vivid flame as Douglas's shell penetrated its ammunition locker. Douglas and Lambert threw themselves down, shielding their heads, as white-hot fragments of metal spattered the countryside. A terrific shock-wave blasted out, jarring every bone in their bodies and almost lifting their own half-track from the ground.

His head reeling, Douglas resumed his position behind the gun and began to traverse the barrel towards the second enemy half-track, but Stan Brough's crew got in the first shot. Their shell exploded on the gun itself and was closely followed by another which exploded in the cab, wrecking it completely. In the flash of the shells the figures of the German gunners could be seen tumbling from the gun platform.

As Conolly's gun finished off the third German half-track, Douglas yelled to Olds to start the engine. A second or two later, he was startled to hear Colette's voice close at hand. She sounded a little plaintive.

'I thought you might have forgotten about me,' she shouted, looking up. 'Can I hitch a ride?'

'Get into the cab,' Douglas shouted back, 'and for God's sake keep your head down! This is likely to be rough.'

He leaned forward around the edge of the gun platform and called out to Olds, who had succeeded in starting the engine and who was now awaiting further orders.

'Get going, Brian! You know what to do.'

Olds reached out and helped Colette, who was having some difficulty, to climb into the cab. Then he found the right gear and sent the half-track lurching round in a semi-circle until it was pointing directly at the perimeter fence.

'Righto, miss,' he said to Colette. 'Let's see how fast this thing will go. But be sure to brace yourself when we hit the fence, mind.'

The vehicle's tracks churned up the soggy ground as Olds accelerated. The other two half-tracks were following in line astern. Douglas and Lambert, clinging desperately to the swaying gun platform, also braced themselves as the barbed-wire fence came at them.

The half-track ripped through it with a screech. Thick strands of barbed wire parted with a vicious twang and Douglas ducked as one of them whip-lashed against the gun, narrowly missing his head. Then they were through and heading out across the airfield, racing parallel with the main runway.

Suddenly, a series of flashes rippled across the far side of the field, beyond the buildings. Lines of tracer flashed through the darkness in both directions as a brisk gun battle flared up between the Maquis, attacking at last, and the German troops responsible for defending the perimeter.

Conolly, seated behind the gun in the third half-track, suddenly spotted a vehicle racing across the aerodrome to intercept them. By this time, there was enough light flickering across the base to identify it as a light armoured car, Type KFZ 222. He knew that it was armed with a quick-firing 20-mm cannon and a 7·92-mm machine gun, that it was much faster than the half-tracks, and that it could do considerable damage.

The KFZ opened fire first, streaks of fire spitting from its gun muzzle. The burst of 20-mm ripped over the top of the middle half-track, several feet too high. Forcing himself to keep cool, Conolly took careful aim and loosed off a whole clip of 37-mm at the armoured car, seeing the flashes as his shells peppered it. It veered away and swayed crazily across the airfield with smoke pouring from it, then stopped abruptly and burst into flames.

Douglas, who had been temporarily distracted by the brief gun battle between Conolly's half-track and the armoured car, had his attention drawn to what was happening up ahead by Lambert.

'Look, sir! There's an aircraft taking off!'

Lambert was right. At the far end of the runway, clearly visible between the lights of the flarepath, a Dornier was starting to accelerate. Douglas leaned over the edge of the gun platform again and instructed Olds to drive straight up the runway towards the bomber. Olds obeyed at once, the half-track swinging on to the tarmac and taking one of the flarepath lights with it. Olds jammed his foot down on the accelerator. Behind the cab, Douglas nestled down behind the gun and lined up the long barrel on the rapidly approaching Dornier, whose tail had now come up from the runway.

In the Dornier's cockpit, Karl Preuss, piloting the first KG100 aircraft to take off, watched in wide-eyed horror as Douglas's half-track raced towards him. His right hand held the throttles wide open at maximum boost and his left held the control column firmly, keeping it pushed slightly forward. In the Dornier's nose, Sergeant Rainer Becher's quiet, unemotional voice read off the airspeed for Preuss's benefit. General von Falkenberg was sitting behind Preuss, looking ahead over the pilot's shoulder. Suddenly, he too spotted the half-track and let out a yell.

'I know!' Preuss shouted. 'Here goes!'

Using both hands, he hauled back the stick and literally wrenched the Dornier off the ground just as the airspeed indicator's needle reached the take-off speed mark. The bomber teetered into the air, its engines – bearing the heavy load of the missiles, as well as the weight of the aircraft and its fuel – fighting the pull of gravity and the drag of the airframe to achieve safe flying speed.

The half-track's gun flashed and a shell struck the runway somewhere underneath the slow-flying aircraft. It wobbled dangerously and Preuss heard several metallic clangs from somewhere astern. He pushed the nose down slightly to restore the forward speed, then pulled back the control column again. The Dornier seemed to falter for a moment, then its propellers bit into the air and it began to climb steadily into the darkness.

Shaken, Preuss circled the airfield, looking down. Gun battles were in progress at several points on the perimeter, but what was more alarming was the sight of one aircraft after another bursting into flames on the ground. As he watched, a Dornier's missiles blew up in a great orange bubble of light, the explosion sending a visible shock wave rippling across the airfield.

'There must be something we can do,' Preuss whispered to himself, although the words were carried to the rest of the crew over the intercom.

'There is nothing!' Von Falkenberg's voice was harsh. 'Set course for the target immediately. That is an order!'

Reluctantly, Preuss turned away from the blazing airfield and headed out over the coast into the Mediterranean.

Callum Douglas swore violently as he saw his shell burst on the runway underneath the Dornier. Moments later, having had no time in which to elevate his gun barrel to the angle necessary for a second shot, he ducked as the aircraft's dark bulk swept low overhead in a thunder of sound.

There was no time to bother about the one that got away. Looking ahead, he saw more Dorniers, a long line of them, taxying towards the take-off point around the perimeter track. One of them was already lining up on the runway and Olds, without being told, headed straight for it. This time there was no mistake: Douglas fired a full clip of shells into the Dornier's dark fuselage and left it in flames, crumpled on a shattered undercarriage. A lake of burning fuel spread out around it and reached its missile warheads. They erupted in a thunderclap of flame and sound that sent fragments of the aircraft hundreds of feet into the air.

Olds swung the half-track clear of the runway and drove at top speed parallel to the perimeter track. Douglas threw a glance to the rear and saw that the other two vehicles were following, their guns in action as Brough and Conolly raked the line of aircraft in their turn.

One or two of the German air gunners, quicker off the mark than the others, had clambered into their turrets and were returning the fire. Lambert slammed another ammunition clip home in Douglas's gun and he opened fire again, concentrating on the Dorniers that were shooting back. At this range, the effect of the 37-mm shells was devastating. They tore through the thin skins of the bombers, exploding in their fuselages and fuel tanks. Crew members who survived jumped down from the burning carcases and ran for their lives between spreading

155

rivers of blazing petrol.

Douglas went on firing as fast as Lambert could reload. He saw some of his shells explode in the cockpit of a moving Dornier and the aircraft veered sharply out of line, its crew dead, its wingtip slicing through the tail of an aircraft in front. It went weaving across the airfield and Olds had to swerve sharply in order to avoid it as it passed in front of the half-track. The Dornier crashed into the side of a hangar. A spout of flame shot from one of its engines and quickly spread along the wing. In its light, Douglas could see figures running from the hangar. Some of them carried guns and loosed off a few ineffectual shots at the speeding half-tracks.

Suddenly there were no more aircraft to shoot at. Douglas looked back again, the other two half-tracks were still chasing him, their guns blasting a few last rounds into what had, in the space of about forty-five seconds, become a long line of blazing wreckage. Everywhere, missile warheads and the highly volatile fuel in their propellant tanks were detonating, scattering fiery debris far and wide.

Douglas shouted to Olds to keep going, straight towards the airfield's western perimeter fence. He could feel the heat from his overworked 37-mm gun wafting back into his face. Lambert slammed another clip of ammunition into place, saying that there were still several clips remaining.

Fire came at them from several points on the perimeter, and bullets clanged against the half-track's armoured sides. Douglas abandoned the 37-mm for the simple reason that he could see no clearly defined target, and instead loosed off a few bursts from his MP-40 in the direction of the enemy fire.

The half-track slammed through the barbed wire on the western side of the airfield, running the gauntlet of more enemy fire as it did so, and headed out into the open country beyond, still followed by the other two. Douglas was relieved that Brough and Conolly had come through all right, and wondered how the Maquisards were faring in their attacks on the northern and eastern fringes of the airfield.

A great pall of smoke, reddened by the flames that fed it,

boiled upwards over Istres. As he clung to the sides of the swaying gun platform, Douglas could hear the klaxons of enemy fire tenders, screeching through the night as they converged on the conflagration. It would be hours before the Germans brought the blaze under control.

As soon as they were well clear of the airfield, lost in the darkness and with no sight or sound of pursuit, Douglas told Olds to halt for a few moments. He jumped down as the other two half-tracks drew up alongside and peered into the cab.

'Well done, Brian,' he said. 'How's Colette?'

It was the woman who answered, and Douglas noted that her voice was weak and shaky. 'I'll be all right,' she said. 'I'm glad that's over, though. What next?'

Douglas wasn't quite sure, but had no intention of admitting it. When planning the attack on the information supplied by Conolly he had worked out a rough escape route, but he had no idea what opposition they were likely to meet. His plans, at this point, did not extend much further than trying to get across the Rhône into the Camargue, where they could with luck lose themselves, and make their way to the south coast. He had no means of knowing whether the Royal Navy's launch would be there to take them off – no inkling, even, whether the Navy had been informed of the revised plan.

He quickly established that everyone in the other two half-tracks had come to no harm, and then outlined his intentions to Brough and Conolly.

'If we keep going on our present heading,' he told them, 'we should hit the road junction I pointed out on the map earlier. The branch of the 'T' leads down to Port-St-Louis, just on this side of the Rhône. The road will quite probably be patrolled, especially at the junction and also at the place where it passes under a canal. We may have to fight our way through, so be alert. The junction is about two miles up front, and we won't rush up to it. Keep a hundred yards spacing, in case we run into trouble. Mount up.'

The half-tracks forged on, coping well with the soggy, low-lying ground. If the crossroads ahead were defended, Douglas

157

was banking on the defenders expecting only an attack by the Maquis; he was taking a gamble that they had not been alerted to look out for three German half-tracks which had just shot up Istres. However, they would certainly know that something had happened; quite apart from the racket caused by the gunfire and explosions, the bonfire on Istres was lighting up the eastern horizon.

Suddenly, without warning, Douglas's eyes were seared by a brilliant light as three powerful flares burst high overhead, throwing the landscape into stark relief. Douglas closed his eyes and then opened them again, cautiously. What he saw made his stomach turn over.

The flares revealed the crossroads, less than two hundred yards ahead. And seated squatly in the middle of the junction, its gun pointed directly at him, was one of the biggest armoured fighting vehicles he had ever seen. Beside him, Lambert let out a gasp.

'What the blazes is that?' he asked. Douglas made no immediate reply, but clambered round the edge of the gun platform so that he could speak to Olds in the cab without shouting.

'Keep going ahead,' he told the driver, 'but slowly. We might just bluff this one through.'

Returning to his original position, he searched his mind for details of the enemy vehicle. 'It's a self-propelled tank destroyer,' he told Lambert quickly. 'A Porsche Ferdinand, by the look of things. Sixty-eight tons, and packing an 88-mm gun along with a 7·92-mm machine-gun. It's got about eight inches of armour at the front, and our 37-mm shells would just bounce off it.'

He was uncomfortably conscious that the half-tracks, from the Ferdinand's vantage point, would be starkly silhouetted against the false dawn of burning Istres. Above, dangling on their parachutes, the flares were still burning fiercely. By their light, on either side of the tank destroyer, he could see a number of helmeted heads which, presumably, belonged to German soldiers crouching in foxholes. They were now within fifty yards of the enemy positions. Suddenly, from somewhere near the end of the German line, a voice yelled: *'Los damit!'*

Douglas knew enough of German military commands to realize that this was the order to open fire. Before he could react, a light machine-gun chattered and glowing tracers streaked around his ears, bouncing off the armoured gun shield and ricocheting away into the night like deadly fireflies.

'Nein!' Another voice shouted. *'Feuer einstellen!'*

The machine-gunner was being told to cease firing. Douglas mentally blessed the trigger-happy German soldier who, with luck, had just prevented them from driving into a trap.

'Olds!' he shouted, 'full speed, and steer left!'

Olds complied immediately, and the half-track slewed around in a shower of mud. At that instant, an orange streak of flame spat from the muzzle of the Ferdinand's 88-mm gun. The shell, a solid armour-piercing round rather than a high-explosive one, struck the turning half-track beneath the gun mounting, blasting away one of its centre wheels and slamming it, a twisted mass of red-hot metal, into the chassis. If the shell had struck a split second earlier, before Olds had started his turn, it would have passed through the engine and most probably killed the two in the cab.

As it was, both Douglas and Lambert were stunned and shaken by the fierce impact. Both fell to their knees on the gun platform, which was now buckled upwards and twisted on its right-hand side. A metallic echo resounded in the air, piercing the brain with its shrillness.

With an effort Douglas pulled himself together, dropping from the platform on the opposite side of the half-track to that facing the tank destroyer. He was followed by Lambert, who was bleeding from a gash where his forehead had made violent contact with the gun breech. The two of them hurried round to the cab, wrenched open the door on the driver's side and hurriedly dragged out the two dazed occupants.

'What happened?' Colette asked faintly, shaking her head to clear it.

'We took a shell from the tank destroyer – that's the thing

on the crossroads,' Douglas told her. 'The only thing we can do for the moment is stay on this side of the half-track and hope its armour is strong enough to stand any more shells.'

But the crew of the Ferdinand, having immobilized Douglas's half-track, were no longer interested in it. Douglas heard the tank destroyer's twin Maybach engines roar, the sound accompanied by a harsh screeching as it swivelled rapidly on its tracks and sighted on Brough's half-track, which had also veered off to the left.

Both Brough and Conolly, whose half-track was keeping formation with the sergeant-major's, had now opened fire on the tank destroyer, but Douglas's prediction was right; their 37-mm shells exploded harmlessly on the Ferdinand's heavy armour plating. The only advantage they had was speed, and they tried to use it as best they could, zigzagging while still maintaining a brisk rate of fire.

But the German gunner in the Ferdinand was good. Crouching helplessly beside his own useless half-track, Douglas heard the tank destroyer's 88-mm bark again and saw the glowing red tail of a tracer round converge on the front of Brough's vehicle. It entered the cab, killing Sansom instantly. The half-track careered wildly out of control and, in the light of more flares sent up by the enemy, Douglas saw Brough and Barber jump clear and throw themselves flat. The abandoned half-track plunged on across country, steadily curving round until it headed back towards Istres, bearing its dead driver.

In the third half-track, Willings, who was driving, had been heading across the front of the German positions on Conolly's orders when the Irishman suddenly shouted to him to turn around. He did so, heading towards the spot where Brough and Barber were lying under the scant cover of some bushes. Positioning the vehicle between the enemy and the stranded SAS men, he slowed down briefly so that they could be hauled up on to the gun platform with the help of Conolly and Mitchell. Then, accelerating once more, he manoeuvred the half-track so that it was shielded from the Ferdinand's deadly gun by the hulk of Douglas's machine. He drove up nose-on

160

to it, so that the vehicles formed two sides of a square, then jumped down, together with the rest of the crew. Given time, he knew that the Ferdinand's gun could batter both vehicles to pieces, but they were relatively safe for the time being. Moreover, the half-tracks would provide cover if the German infantry attacked.

Douglas, Brough and Conolly looked at one another in the light of the flares. This time, there was no way out. The ground afforded scarcely any cover, and if they tried to run for it they would be cut down before they had gone twenty yards. All they could do was stay put and wait for the inevitable assault. When it came, they would try and take as many of the enemy as possible with them.

And Douglas, at that moment, made one of the hardest decisions of his life. When the end came, he resolved to put a bullet through Colette's brain before he went down fighting. He would not allow her to live merely to undergo the nightmare of torture before the enemy finally killed her.

The tank destroyer's engines roared again, accompanied by a rumbling clatter. Although they could not see it, they knew that its great bulk was beginning to move inexorably forward, bearing down to sweep the half-tracks aside and crush the life out of their former occupants.

In those moments, wild thoughts flashed through Douglas's mind. He wondered if he might be able to jump on to the Ferdinand and drop a grenade down its hatch, but knew in the same instant that he would stand no chance. Better to lead his men in a last, wild charge against the German infantry.

'Get ready, boys,' he said quietly. At the same time, surreptitiously, he moved the muzzle of his MP-40 close to Colette's head. He would have to close his eyes when he did it.

Suddenly, a storm of firing erupted from the German positions. This was it, then; the final assault. This was where it all ended. His finger began to tighten on the trigger of his machine-pistol.

Then he realized that no bullets were crackling around the half-tracks, and that the shouts that were coming from the

161

enemy were not battle-cries, but screams of pain and terror. He hurled himself to the rear of the sheltering half-track and looked around it, crouching on one knee. An extraordinary sight met his eyes.

The Ferdinand was some thirty yards away, still grinding slowly forward. On its massive armoured casing two men were balanced. In his right hand, each held something aloft – something with a small, flickering flame at one end. A moment later, as though on a given signal, one of the men wrenched open the Ferdinand's hatch – which no one had taken the trouble to fasten from the inside – and both hurled their missiles into the crew compartment.

Even above the roar of the Ferdinand's engine, Douglas could hear the frantic, high-pitched screaming from inside the tank destroyer as the Molotov cocktails turned its interior into an inferno. The men who had thrown them jumped down from the casing and ran alongside the still moving vehicle, unslinging Sten guns from their shoulders.

A man emerged from the hatch, screaming wildly, beating at the flames that engulfed him. A short burst of Sten fire caught him and he collapsed, hanging face down over the casing. Another man tried to push past the body and met the same fate. The two men who had thrown the petrol bombs turned and began to run quickly away from the Ferdinand, aware what was going to happen next.

The tank destroyer was almost on top of Douglas's half-tracks when its stored 80-mm ammunition detonated with a shattering roar. The earth heaved and great chunks of armoured casing shrieked through the air. Douglas and the others flung themselves to one side as the blast wave caught the half-tracks, heaving them violently sideways. For an instant, it seemed as though one of them was going to topple over, but it righted itself and settled back on its tracks again.

Groggily, Douglas and the others got to their feet, Colette being helped upright by Brough. Apart from some sporadic single shots, the firing from the German positions had ceased. Advancing round the rear of the half-track, Douglas came face to face with a man carrying a Sten gun – one of those, he thought, who had thrown the Molotov cocktails. He stood silhouetted in the glare of the wrecked and fiercely blazing tank destroyer.

'It seems we got here just in time,' he said in a cultured English accent. 'I am Auguste. You, I presume, are Captain Douglas?'

'That's right,' Douglas said, shaking the man's hand. 'And I can't begin to say how glad I am to see you.'

Auguste smiled in the light of the flames. 'Quite all right, old boy. I see you did quite a job on Istres. No time to talk about that now, though; we've got to get going. German reinforcements are starting to pour into the area. That's the bad news. The good news is that the Royal Navy MTB will be picking you up from the Camargue coast at first light – if you can get there in time. You'd better get your men together. There's still a long way to go.'

'We've still got one half-track,' Conolly pointed out. 'It hasn't got much fuel left, but it's good for another few miles.'

'Excellent,' Auguste said. 'Incidentally, my men are holding the road as far as Port-St-Louis. We've also commandeered a barge to take you across the Rhône. Everything depends on how long we can hold off the Germans; they are already in Arles and are probably moving south at this very moment. Once you are across the Rhône and in the Camargue you'll be safe enough; they can't follow you there.'

'But what about you and your men?' Douglas wanted to know.

'We'll be crossing the river, too,' Auguste said, 'once we've seen you safely on your way. Afterwards, we'll be dispersing northwards into Languedoc for a while until things quieten down again. Anyway, who knows? We might be kicking the Germans out of France in a few months' time.'

'I hope so,' Douglas said. 'Anyway, thanks again for your help. Maybe we'll meet again in more favourable circumstances. One last thing – you'd better give us an escort of some sort, otherwise your chaps might get trigger-happy when they

163

see a German half-track trundling down the road towards them.'

'Here's your escort,' Auguste told him, as a man came striding up to stand in the light of the blazing tank. He carried a German Mauser 98 rifle slung across his shoulder.

Colette, who had been leaning weakly against the half-track, gave a gasp of recognition and took a few short steps forward to embrace the man. It was Etienne Barbut.

'Tell him I'm glad to see he's alive and well,' Douglas instructed her. 'And now let's move, before things get un-healthy.'

Colette and Barbut climbed into the cab of the half-track alongside Willings, who once again volunteered to do the driving. Douglas and the remaining SAS men clambered on to the gun platform, where they were joined by two or three Maquisards, each armed with a Sten and wearing a bandolier into which were stuffed German 'potato-masher' stick gren-ades.

Willings drove past the shattered Ferdinand and over the crossroads, which were littered with dead Germans. Cheering Maquisards, holding their guns aloft, saluted the half-track and its occupants as it churned past, and some ran alongside for a while before dropping back.

The vehicle drove steadily on past more patrols, slowing down as each one was approached so that Barbut could call out to the Maquisards. Half an hour later, having passed under a canal, it came to another crossroads and its occupants climbed down. Barbut spoke rapidly with Colette, who trans-lated.

'This is as far as we go,' she told Douglas, 'at least in the half-track. The left-hand fork goes down into Port-St-Louis, the other follows the Rhône to Arles. We go on across country for a mile or so before reaching the river.'

As she finished speaking, there came a sudden outburst of firing from along the Arles road. It was still some miles away, Douglas guessed, but there was no telling how long it would be before the Maquisards who were holding the road succumbed to mounting enemy pressure. He indicated the Resistance fighters who had accompanied them on the half-track, and said to Colette:

'Tell them we've no longer any use for the vehicle. It's theirs. No doubt its firepower will come in handy. And tell Monsieur Barbut to come with us.'

After a further exchange of words, Colette turned back to Douglas in obvious distress.

'It's no use,' she said. 'I've pleaded with him, but he insists on staying. He says that his place is with the Maquisards.'

Douglas nodded, understanding. Wordlessly, he reached out and grasped Barbut's hand, then turned away to lead his men across the mile of ground to the Rhône. Unseen by Douglas, Colette clung to Barbut for a few moments and kissed him before also turning away. No one, in the darkness, saw the tears that were coursing down her cheeks.

The ground was soft and boggy, and water reached over their ankles as they trudged on, the men taking it in turns to support the ailing Colette. At last they reached the river and waded through the marshy flats towards it, gazing with trepidation at its sluggish expanse. Douglas judged that it was at least half a mile across, which would not have presented a problem had it not been for one fact. There was no sign of the barge that was to have taken them to the far bank.

'Something's obviously gone wrong,' Douglas said, 'but we can't afford to hang about here.' He threw a glance upriver, where he could see flashes twinkling in the darkness. The sound of firing from the Arles road was becoming more intense. 'We'll just have to swim for it, that's all.'

A half-mile swim was well within the capability of all his men, but there was Colette to be considered. She looked at him, knowing what he was thinking.

'Leave me,' she said bravely. 'I told you that I would be a burden to you. Leave me here.'

'Not on your life,' Douglas told her firmly. 'You've come this far with us, and you're coming the rest of the way. These overalls are designed to provide some buoyancy, and we'll hold on to you.'

'Do we ditch our weapons, sir?' The question came from Mitchell, who was still burdened with his beloved radio set as well as his MP-40.

'No, we don't,' Douglas told him. 'We swim with them. You've all been trained to do that. Your wireless will have to go, though, Mitch.'

The Rhodesian signaller paused, then unstrapped the set, held it between his hands for a few moments, and finally hurled it as far as he could into the river. Without waiting to be ordered, he strode down the shallow bank and into the water. The rest followed suit, Douglas staying close to Colette.

From a hiding place among some bushes on the far bank, a man watched the swimmers' progress through a pair of Zeiss night-glasses. He saw their heads bobbing up and down, and noted how one of the swimmers seemed to be supporting another. It should not be difficult to snare them, he thought with satisfaction, drumming his fingertips against the casing of the binoculars.

'Shall we open fire on your signal, monsieur?' The question came from one of the dozen or so militiamen who lay nearby, their carbines at the ready. The Gestapo man rounded on him furiously.

'You idiot!' He snapped. 'How many times must I tell you, you will not open fire at all! My intention is to capture those swine alive; I have planned for that ever since I discovered the tracks of their aeroplane, days ago. When they come out of the river you will surround them and take them prisoner. That is all.'

He resumed his vigil with the night-glasses. The others strained their eyes in the darkness, unable as yet to see anything at all. The roll of gunfire from the direction of Arles made a constant background noise.

The swimmers ploughed valiantly on through the Rhône's current, unaware of the fate that awaited them. The Gestapo man continued to watch them, speaking softly to himself, mentally urging them on. They were almost at the bank now,

166

almost at the place where the water became shallow enough for them to wade ashore. Soon it would be all over. The Gestapo man glowed inwardly at the thought of the praise and promotion that would be bestowed on him for this night's work.

And soon over it all was, but not in the way he envisaged. The voice of the guns masked a closer sound, and the first indication the Gestapo man and the Milice had of the peril that was bearing down on them came when the ground suddenly began to tremble beneath their prone bodies. The Gestapo man released his binoculars and got to his knees, startled, and his last vision in this world was of the flying, razor-sharp hooves that cut him down.

The tide of white horses swept over the militiamen, and long machetes gleamed dully in the night as the *gardiens* slashed to left and right, sending the hated Milice screaming and scattering. None fired a shot; those who survived the murderous onslaught threw aside their rifles and fled into the darkness, or the temporary sanctuary of the river.

Douglas and the others, hearing the commotion, halted their progress and trod water, looking at the darkened river bank in alarm. Then a voice hailed them out of the night, and Douglas, exhausted as he was, kissed Colette's soaked hair and laughed aloud in relief.

The voice was that of Raoul.

Hands reached out, a minute later, to drag them from the water. The horses stood passively, ignoring the trampled bodies of the militiamen.

'Quickly,' Raoul urged them. 'Mount up and ride! Nothing can touch you now. You've done it, by God! The boat is on its way in. The *gardiens* will go with you, so that you don't miss the place. Go now, and good luck!'

They dragged their soaked bodies on to the backs of the patient horses. Colette sat in front of Douglas, who held on to her firmly. The horses got into their stride, cantering through the marshes, their hoofbeats dulled by the soft ground so that they seemed for all the world like phantom creatures,

167

sliding through the dark towards the coast, their manes and tails lifting with their rippling motion.

And in the Camargue, a new legend was born.

The Dornier droned steadily on in the darkness, skirting the Balearic Islands at 10,000 feet. Hardly a word had been spoken since take-off; even von Falkenberg was silent, although Karl Preuss sensed that the general's mind was already probing all the possibilities of finding a scapegoat on whom to pin the blame for the disaster that had overwhelmed the remainder of KG100 at Istres.

Preuss was not happy with the way the bomber was handling. The controls felt sloppy, and he suspected that the shell that had burst underneath the aircraft on take-off had caused some damage to the control cables in the rear of the fuselage.

Whatever they, the crew of the solitary Dornier, might achieve now would amount to little more than a pinprick, Preuss thought moodily. If they were lucky they might sink a couple of ships, but that was all. The Allied convoy would still forge ahead to its destination, wherever that might be. Had it not been for the presence of von Falkenberg, he would have aborted the mission and turned back long ago.

He was worried about the fuel state, too. The engines seemed to be consuming more petrol than was usual. That was an item of information he intended to keep to himself for the time being; the morale of the crew must be low enough as it was, and he had no wish to burden them further with the knowledge that they might not make it back home.

The Dornier was fifty miles south-west of Formentera, still on course for Gibraltar, when the real trouble started. The first hint came with an urgent call over the intercom from the flight engineer.

'Sir, the starboard engine is starting to overheat badly. The temperature has been fluctuating for some time, but now it has suddenly gone into the red.'

Preuss acknowledged and throttled back the troublesome

motor, applying some rudder to compensate for the aircraft's sudden tendency to swing. At the same time, he glanced across at the engine itself, leaning forward in his straps and craning his neck as he did so, for the wing and the engines were positioned well to the rear of the cockpit and it was not easy to see them from the pilot's seat.

What he saw made a sick knot of fear grip his stomach. The cowling of the starboard engine was glowing redly in the darkness.

Preuss ordered the flight engineer to shut down the engine and apply the fire extinguisher. Almost at once, the aircraft slowly began to lose altitude. From behind Preuss, von Falkenberg demanded to know what was happening.

'We've got the beginnings of a fire in the starboard engine,' Preuss told the general. 'I've had it shut down, which means that I can no longer hold altitude. I'm going to have to jettison the missiles and turn back.'

'No!' Von Falkenberg's voice rose almost to a scream. 'I forbid it! You must press on to the target at all cost!'

'Can't be done, General,' Preuss said laconically. 'We'd never make it. Rainer, get ready to jettison the weapons.'

In the nose, Rainer Becher's hand hovered over the switches that would release the Fritz-z missiles. Without their weight, the Dornier might stay in the air long enough to make an emergency landing in neutral Spain.

'No!' von Falkenberg yelled again. 'You heard my orders! Continue to the target. You forget that I too am a pilot, Preuss!'

'Look out, sir.' It was the navigator who spoke. Preuss half turned in his seat. Von Falkenberg was on his feet, and the pistol in his hand was pointing at Preuss's head.

There was a sudden sharp crack and Preuss threw himself against the side of the cockpit, an involuntary cry bursting from him. Then tremors of heat and cold ran through his body as he realized that he was still alive.

He looked down. The upper half of Rainer Becher lay on the flight deck, his legs still in the nose compartment. He held a smoking Luger. General von Falkenberg lay on the floor, sprawled across the entry hatch that gave access to the flight deck.

The navigator came forward and bent over the general. A moment later a blast of freezing air roared into the cockpit as the hatch was opened. Then it was slammed shut again. When Preuss looked round, the navigator was back in his seat and the general was gone.

Becher jettisoned the missiles and the Dornier, although still losing height, was now losing it more slowly. Carefully, Preuss swung the nose round towards Spanish territory.

After a minute or two of silence, he said: 'We've been together a long time. Long enough to get our story straight. About the general, I mean.'

'The general?' said the navigator. 'I could have sworn he was on one of the other aircraft. Probably got blown to bits.'

'Yes,' said Rainer Becher. 'What general?'

He spoke for all of them.

EPILOGUE

The news from Italy was not good. The Allied invasion force had gone ashore on the Anzio beaches on schedule and at first had met little opposition, but the Germans had reacted with unexpected swiftness and now, early in February 1944, the Anglo-American divisions were engaged in bitter fighting and unable to break out from the beach-head they had established. It seemed that the war would not be shortened, after all.

Douglas had told Colette none of this when he visited her in the military hospital on Gibraltar. She was recovering from a severe bout of pneumonia, and the doctors had stressed that she was not to be upset in any way. So he had sat there beside her bed and held her hand, and made small talk until she had drifted off into an uneasy sleep.

He walked slowly down the hospital steps, narrowing his eyes against the sun, lost in his own thoughts. He did not really see the tall figure ascending the steps towards him until a familiar voice greeted him.

'Well, Douglas. And how is she?'

Startled, Douglas looked up and a moment later threw a hasty salute in the general direction of Brigadier Masters.

'Improving, sir, thank you,' he said. 'But she has to take things very quietly for another week or two. She hasn't to have any worries. I didn't know you were here,' he added.

'Oh, I've a job or two to take care of in Gib,' the brigadier told him cryptically. 'By the way, it was a good show you put up in France. A very good show indeed. KG100 won't be troubling anybody for a long time, I fancy.'

Masters frowned suddenly. 'You said that Colette has to take things easily – no sudden shocks, or anything like that?'

'That's right, sir. Why – is there something wrong?'

Masters put his hand in a pocket and pulled out a buff telegram envelope.

'I came to give her this,' he explained. 'But maybe it's not advisable just at the moment. Will you be seeing her again – when she's a little better, I mean?'

'Yes, sir. In fact, I understand we'll both be going home on the same aircraft in a couple of weeks' time, when my leave is over, I could have gone already, but I thought I would stay and – well, you know how it is.' To his embarrassment, he found himself blushing.

Masters nodded. 'So that's the way of it,' he said smilingly. 'Well, good luck to you, Douglas.' His expression grew sombre. 'Maybe she'll need all the comfort she can get,' he said. 'Give her this when she's in better health, will you? Break it to her gently. It's open, so you can read it.'

He handed Douglas the envelope. The SAS officer opened the flap and extracted the single message sheet. The few words stared up at him starkly. The signal was from SOE Headquarters in London, and was addressed to Colette personally.

REGRET INFORM YOU ETIENNE BARBUT CAPTURED AND EXECUTED BY GESTAPO. DEEPEST SYMPATHY.

And that was all.

Douglas turned his face away, full of emotion. 'Damn,' he said softly. 'Damn it to hell. He was a brave man. None of us would have got away without him.'

'He was much more than that to Colette,' Masters said.

Douglas looked at him, puzzled, and asked what he meant.

There was genuine amazement in Masters' voice. 'You mean Colette never told you? Good God, man. Etienne Barbut was her father.'